*Petrochemical
Manufacturing & Marketing Guide
Volume I: Aromatics & Derivatives*

PETROCHEMICAL
Manufacturing &
Marketing Guide
Volume I:
Aromatics & Derivatives

by
ROBERT B. STOBAUGH, JR.
Consultant
Newtonville, Massachusetts

GULF PUBLISHING COMPANY
HOUSTON, TEXAS

Petrochemical Manufacturing & Marketing Guide

Volume I: Aromatics & Derivatives

Copyright© 1966 by Gulf Publishing Co., Houston, Texas

Library of Congress Catalog Card No. 67-24629

Manufactured in the United States of America

To Beverly

without whose encouragement this
book would never have been written.

Preface

There has long been a need for one published source containing a detailed discussion of the business and technical aspects of the more important petrochemicals. I believe that this book is the first attempt to meet that need.

This first volume of *Petrochemical Manufacturing & Marketing Guide* covers aromatics and derivatives of aromatics; Volume Two will cover olefins, diolefins, and acetylene.

Each petrochemical is covered in a separate chapter, and the entire industry is summarized in the final chapter. Conditions are described as of 1965-66 and the key variables are projected to 1970.

The book is intended to be used as a basic reference by a broad segment of petrochemical management, especially those engaged in financial analysis, marketing, purchasing, commercial development, marketing research, and engineering.

Although this work was not specifically designed for use by the academic profession, the material is now being used in courses on production management and chemical economics in both business and engineering schools.

There is a paucity of reliable information published about the petrochemical industry. Accurate estimates of plant capacities and markets especially are lacking, even United States Government statistics are not totally reliable. This is evidenced by the production data given for naphthalene and phthalic anhydride. Because of such factors, the book obviously should not be used as a substitute for careful research and analysis on specific problems.

I wish to acknowledge the encouragement given to this endeavor by Mr. Thomas C. Ponder, Petrochemicals Editor of *Hydrocarbon Processing*. The work was first published in that magazine in a series of articles between September 1965 and May 1966.

Robert B. Stobaugh, Jr.

Newtonville, Mass.
August 1966

Contents

*Petrochemical
Manufacturing & Marketing Guide
Volume I: Aromatics & Derivatives*

1

Benzene

PETROLEUM SOURCES provide 80 percent of the U.S. benzene and will provide an even greater percentage in the future. Consumption of U.S. benzene is expected to grow 8 percent a year between 1965 and 1970 resulting in a 1970 demand of 1,150 million gallons versus 800 million gallons[4] in 1965. Styrene monomer will continue to be the largest user of benzene followed by cyclohexane and phenol. All other users are relatively small. Economics indicate that benzene price in the next few years should be in the 25-cent to 28-cent-a-gallon range although action by the U.S. Government on Foreign Trade Zones and Puerto Rican import quotas could result in a lower price. The total value of benzene produced in the U.S. has grown from $100 million in the mid-50s to $200 million in 1965 and is expected to hit $300 milion in 1970. Ample petroleum raw materials are available to provide the required benzene; the question not yet clearly answered is the particular type of petroleum raw material to be used.

MANUFACTURE

Benzene is obtained from five main sources:

Petroleum refinery reformers	58%
Dealkylation of toluene	22%
Cokeoven light oils	13%
Ethylene plant drip oils	5%
Coaltar	2%
	100%

These figures are based on estimates of 1965 production in the U.S. It is interesting to note that only 15 percent of U.S. benzene is produced by the steel and coal industries while the remaining 85 percent is from the petrochemical industry. As recently as 1958 the steel and coal industries produced more benzene than did the petrochemical industry! This illustrates the rapid growth of the petroleum industry and its capture of the chemicals industry from the steel and coal industries.

There will be two processes discussed here: Benzene from refinery reformate and benzene from dealkylation of toluene. The benzene obtained from ethylene plant drip oils is usually recovered by the same method as refinery-reformate benzene; therefore, a discussion of benzene from refinery reformate also covers benzene from ethylene plant drip oils.

Benzene from Refinery Reformate. There are five major steps in the manufacture of benzene from refinery reformate; these are shown in Figure 1-1. The chemistry is shown in Figure 1-2.

In the first step a straight-run gasoline fraction (100°-390° F ASTM) is fed to a hydrogen pretreatment unit in order to remove sulfur compounds; the need for this treatment varies with the character of the crude oil.

In the second step the gasoline is separated in a distillation train into at least three different streams: (1) Pentanes and lighter, which go to gasoline, (2) the heart-

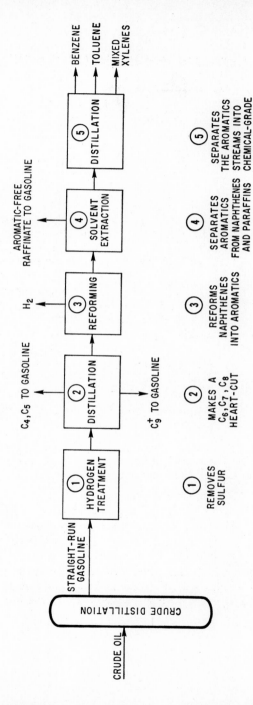

Figure 1-1. To obtain benzene from a petroleum refinery by reforming, use this typical processing scheme.

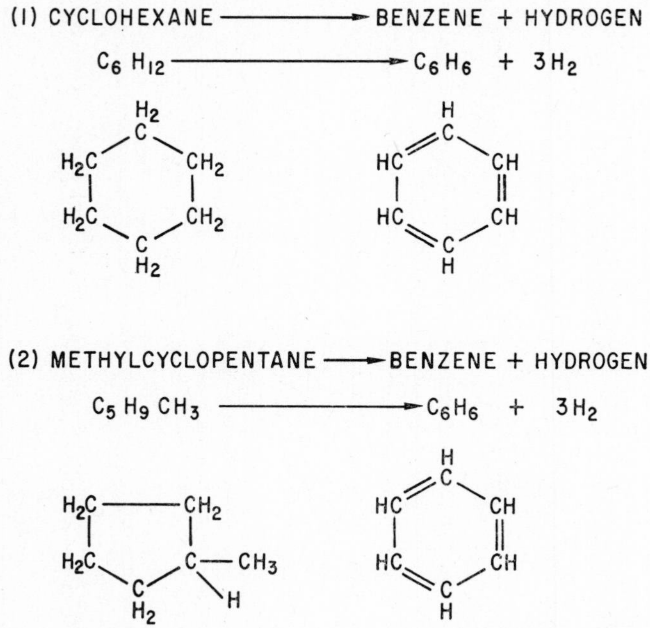

(1) CYCLOHEXANE ⟶ BENZENE + HYDROGEN

C_6H_{12} ⟶ C_6H_6 + $3H_2$

(2) METHYLCYCLOPENTANE ⟶ BENZENE + HYDROGEN

$C_5H_9CH_3$ ⟶ C_6H_6 + $3H_2$

Figure 1-2. Typical reactions when producing benzene from refinery naphthenes by reforming.

cut containing the C_6, C_7, and C_8 (150°-300°F ASTM), and (3) the C_9 and heavier materials, which go to gasoline. This scheme is used when it is desired to maximize the production of aromatics; however, if this is not the case then a more complex distillation train may be used to separate the C_6, C_7, and C_8 materials into individual cuts in order to feed one or more cuts to the reformer to maximize the production of the aromatics of a particular carbon number. Usually the C_6, C_7, and C_8 are reformed when benzene is being manufactured; however, when benzene is not to be manufactured the unit will not be designed to reform the C_6's as a C_6 aromatic does not have sufficient octane value in excess of a C_6 naphthene to justify reforming.

In the third step naphthenes are converted to aromatics over a platinum catalyst; reaction conditions vary according to the process but a popular one uses a reactor temperature in the range of 850-980°F at pressures of 200-800 psig. This step also results in secondary reactions such as isomerization and dehydrocyclization, both of which improve gasoline octane.

These first three steps are used in most refineries in order to increase gasoline value, regardless of whether benzene is being manufactured; however, the remaining two steps, to be discussed next, are used only when benzene is to be manufactured. In step four, aromatics are separated from the paraffins and residual naphthenes by dissolving in aqueous diethylene glycol; the pure aromatics in turn are stripped from the glycol. The details of this process are shown in the flow diagram in Figure 1-3.

Step five is the final fractionation and purification of the aromatics streams. This is shown in Figure 1-3 also. The stream passes through a clay-treat tower and then final fractionation is accomplished in order to separate the benzene, toluene, and xylene stream.

The economics of these operations are discussed in a separation section.

Benzene from Dealkylation of Toluene. The flow diagram for this process is shown in Figure 1-4. The chemistry of benzene production from toluene and xylenes is shown in Figure 1-5; however, in the United States it is more economical to dealkylate toluene than xylenes because toluene has a lower sales value than xylenes and also requires less hydrogen than xylenes in the dealkyla-

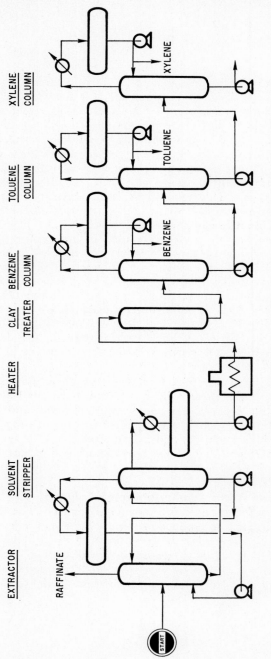

Figure 1-3. Benzene is extracted from refinery reformate using the well known Udex process.

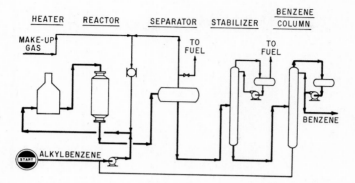

Figure 1-4. Hydrodealkylation of toluene produces benzene using the well known Hydeal process.

tion reaction. It is believed that some of the aromatics complexes to be built in Puerto Rico will dealkylate xylenes as well as benzene.

In the dealkylation process hydrogen is combined with toluene and the combined feed is brought to reaction temperature and charged to the reactor. The reactor effluent is cooled, charged to a separator to remove the hydrogen, and then to a stabilizer for stripping of hydrocarbons lighter than benzene. The benzene product, better than nitration grade, is taken overhead from the final column. Yields are about 96-98 percent of theoretical; thus about 80 gallons of benzene are made per 100 gallons of toluene feed.

The economics of this operation are discussed in a separate section.

U.S. Benzene Producers: These are listed in Table 1-1.

MARKETS

The markets for U.S. benzene are projected to grow about 8 percent a year over the next five years, from an

TABLE 1-1—U.S. Benzene Producers from Petroleum Feedstock

Company	Location	Process	Benzene—Capacity—millions of gallons/yr.
Allied	Winnie, Tex.	Reformer	4
Amoco*	Texas City, Tex.	Reformer	15
Ashland	N. Tonawanda, N.Y.	Reformer	10
	Catlettsburg, Ky.	Reformer	14
		Dealkylation	6
Atlantic-Richfield	Wilmington, Calif.	Reformer	18
Atlas	Shreveport, La.	Reformer	10
Chevron	El Segundo, Calif.	Reformer	25
	Richmond, Calif.	Reformer	10
Continental	Lake Charles, La.	Reformer	6
	Ponca City, Okla.	Reformer	6
Cosden*	Big Spring, Tex.	Reformer	9
		Dealkylation	20
Crown Central	Houston, Tex.	Reformer	5
		Dealkylation	13
Dow	Bay City, Mich.	Buy B-T stream	7
		Dealkylation	13
	Freeport, Tex.	Dealkylation	30
Enjay*	Baton Rouge, La.	Reformer & Ethylene Plant Drip Oils	24
	Baytown, Tex.	Reformer	25
		Dealkylation	30
Gulf*	Philadelphia, Pa.	Reformer	15
		Dealkylation	12
	Port Arthur, Tex.	Reformer	32
Hess	Corpus Christi, Tex.	Reformer & Ethylene Plant Drip Oils	30
Leonard	Mount Pleasant, Mich.	Reformer	3
Marathon	Texas City, Tex.	Reformer	6

TABLE 1-1—Continued

Company	Location	Process	Benzene Capacity— millions of gallons/yr.
Mobil*	Beaumont, Tex.	Reformer & Ethylene Plant Drip Oils	30
Monsanto*	Alvin, Tex.	Reformer & Ethylene Plant Drip Oils	40
		Dealkylation	25
Phillips*	Sweeny, Tex.	Reformer	22
Pontiac	Corpus Christi, Tex.	Reformer	9
Shell*	Houston, Tex.	Reformer	31
	Odessa, Tex.	Reformer	5
		Dealkylation	15
	Wilmington, Calif.	Reformer	15
	Wood River, Ill.	Reformer	30
Signal	Houston, Tex.	Reformer	10
		Dealkylation	12
South Hampton	Silsbee, Tex.	Dealkylation	6
Sun	Marcus Hook, Pa.	Reformer	15
Sunray DX	Tulsa, Okla.	Reformer	11
		Dealkylation	12
Suntide	Corpus Christi, Tex.	Reformer	10
		Dealkylation	15
Tenneco	Chalmette, La.	Reformer	15
Texaco*	Port Arthur, Tex.	Reformer	30
Union Carbide*	S. Charleston, W. Va.	Ethylene Plant Drip Oils	10
Union-Atlantic	Nederland, Tex.	Reformer	18
Union Oil	Lemont, Ill.	Reformer	22
Vickers	Potwin, Kan.	Reformer	3

Total From Petroleum Feedstocks......... 809

Total From 18 Cokeoven Producers and
3 Tar Distillers...................... 142

Grand Total........................... 951

Table 1-1 continued on next page

TABLE 1-1—Continued

Company	Location	Process	Benzene Capacity— millions of gallons/yr.
Announced Capacity, to be added in 1966/1967:			
Cities Service	Lake Charles, La.	Reformer Dealkylation	36 19
Coastal States*	Corpus Christi, Tex.	Reformer	6
Gulf	Port Arthur, Tex.	Dealkylation & Ethylene Plant Drip Oils	25
South-western	Corpus Christi, Tex.	Reformer	6
Texaco	Port Arthur, Tex.	Reformer	15

Total announced new capacity, 1966/1967 . .   107

Grand Total, all U.S. capacity end of 1967 . .   1058

* See Reference 5 at end of chapter.

TABLE 1-2—Markets for U.S. Benzene, 1965 and 1970

	Millions of Gallons	
	1965	1970
Styrene	300	440
Phenol	162	213
Cyclohexane	160	350
Detergent alkylate	28	25
Aniline	23	27
Maleic Anhydride	18	24
DDT	17	17
Export	40	0
Other	52	54
TOTAL	800[4]	1150

(1) TOLUENE + HYDROGEN ⟶ BENZENE + METHANE

$$C_6H_5CH_3 + H_2 \longrightarrow C_6H_6 + CH_4$$

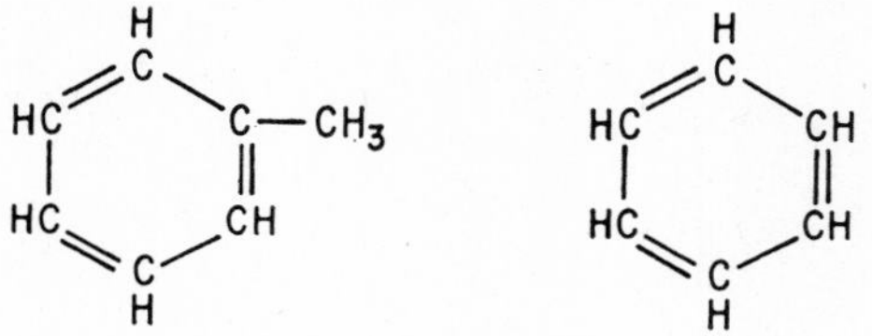

(2) XYLENES + HYDROGEN ⟶ BENZENE + METHANE

$$C_6H_4(CH_3)_2 + 2H_2 \longrightarrow C_6H_6 + 2CH_4$$

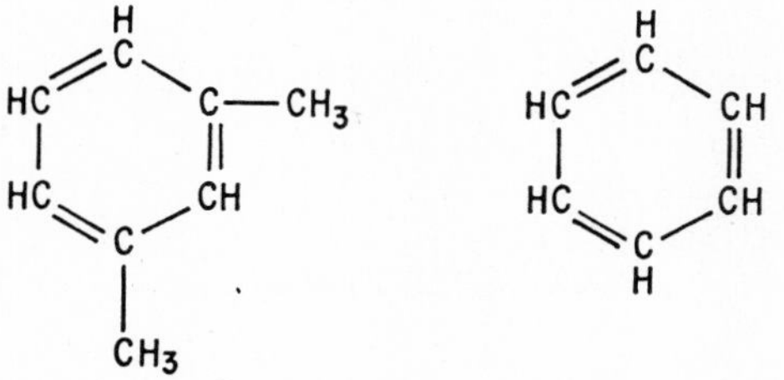

(META-XYLENE IS SHOWN; MIXTURE OF ORTHO, META & PARA IS USED)

Figure 1-5. Typical reactions when producing benzene from toluene and xylenes.

estimated 800 million gallons[4] in 1965 to 1,150 million gallons in 1970. This is in spite of the fact that during this period exports of benzene are expected to drop from 40 million gallons in 1965 to zero in 1970 (See Table 1-2 and Figure 1-6).

The three major consumers of benzene are styrene monomer, cyclohexane and phenol; this will still be the case in 1970 although cyclohexane will become a more

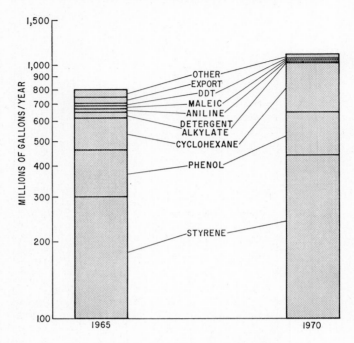

Figure 1-6. U.S. Markets for benzene follow this pattern.

important user than it is in 1965. The markets for these materials along with other chemicals made from benzene are discussed below.

Styrene Monomer. For some time experts have been predicting that consumption of U.S. styrene monomer would cease to grow because of a probable drop in styrene consumption in styrene-butadiene rubber (SBR). However, this leveling off of styrene monomer demand has not yet taken place and is not expected to do so between now and 1970. In fact, styrene production in the

U.S. should grow from an estimated 2.8 billion pounds[7] in 1965 to 4.1 billion pounds[7] in 1970, or an annual growth rate of 8 percent. It will account for about 38 percent of benzene consumption in both 1965 and 1970.

Styrene resins are expected to account for 59 percent of styrene consumption in 1965; this percentage should increase to 70 percent by 1970 as styrene resin consumption will be increasing at an average annual growth rate of 11 percent. The total styrene resin market is split as follows:

General purpose polystyrene	43%
Impact polystyrene	39%
ABS (acrylonitrile-butadiene-styrene), SAN (styrene-acrylonitrile), and Miscellaneous	18%

Styrene-butadiene rubber (SBR) will account for 20 percent of styrene consumption in 1965, but is expected to grow less than overall styrene growth between now and 1970, so will decrease to 14 percent of styrene consumed by 1970. The reason SBR growth is slackening is that polybutadiene and ethylene-propylene rubbers are expected to become more competitive in comparison with SBR.

Polyesters will show rapid growth between now and 1970 but will still account for only 7 percent of styrene use in 1970. Miscellaneous uses and export will continue to account for a small percent of styrene use; in fact, export markets for styrene monomer will be very small in 1970 because of the increased competition from the large-scale plants which will be built in Europe.

About 90 percent of styrene monomer is produced from benzene; the remainder is produced from ethylbenzene extracted from refinery streams rather than made from ethylene and benzene. A list of styrene monomer producers is shown in Table 1-3; this table also lists approximate benzene consumption in 1965.

TABLE 1-3—U.S. Styrene Monomer Producers

Company	Location	Styrene Capacity— millions of pounds/yr.	Estimated Benzene Consumption in 1965 millions of gallons/yr.[1]
Amoco Chem.	Texas City, Tex.	250	19
Cosden*	Big Spring, Tex.	100	7[2]
Dow	Freeport, Tex.	500	55
	Midland, Mich.	300	33
El Paso	Odessa, Tex.	80	9
Foster Grant	Baton Rouge, La.	200	22
Marbon*	Baytown, Tex.	75	0[3]
Monsanto*	Texas City, Tex.	600	61[2]
Shell	Torrance, Calif.	210	23
Sinclair-Koppers	Kobuta, Pa.	200	22
	Houston, Tex.	70	0[3]
Suntide	Corpus Christi	60	4[2]
Union Carbide	Institute, W. Va.	110	12[4]
	Seadrift, Tex.	300	33
TOTAL U.S...............		3055	300

[1] Unless otherwise noted the ethylbenzene is made by alkylation of benzene with ethylene; styrene is made by dehydrogenation of ethylbenzene. Using this route 0.865 pounds of benzene are used per pound of styrene.
[2] Some ethylbenzene obtained by fractionating a petroleum stream.
[3] All ethylbenzene obtained by fractionating a petroleum stream.
[4] Ethylbenzene is oxidized to acetophenone, which is hydrogenated to phenylethyl alcohol, which in turn is dehydrated to styrene.

* See Reference 5 at end of chapter.

Cyclohexane. Markets for U.S. cyclohexane have been increasing dramatically and this is expected to be the case between now and 1970. Consumption in 1965 is expected to be 250 million gallons[7]; this is expected to increase to 460 million gallons by 1970, or an annual growth rate of 13 percent. It will thus account for 350 million gallons of benzene consumption in 1970, up from 160 million gallons in 1965; or 30 percent of total benzene consumption in 1970 versus 25 percent in 1965. However, this forecast is on the basis that cyclohexane will continue to be exported in large quantities; if a faster-than-exected buildup of foreign cyclohexane capacity shuts off exports, U.S. cyclohexane production in 1970 would not exceed that of 1965.

Nylon. Cyclohexane's main outlet is in nylons; 41 percent of total use in Nylon 66 manufacture in the U.S. Nylon 66 is made from cyclohexane by going through cyclohexanone-cyclohexanol, adipic acid, and hexamethylenediamine. A recent development which could slow but not stop cyclohexane growth in Nylon 66 is the Monsanto process for the manufacture of adiponitrile from acrylonitrile by a new electrochemical process. Adiponitrile in turn is used to make hexamethylenediamine. Thus one-half of the Nylon 66 molecule will come from acrylonitrile rather than cyclohexane; the other half will continue to come from cyclohexane.

A rapidly-growing market for cyclohexane is in Nylon 6; in this case, cyclohexane is used to make caprolactam which is the monomer for Nylon 6. Some 7 percent of cyclohexane is used in this market in the U.S.; however, 45 percent of total U.S. cyclohexane is exported and most of this is used in Nylon 6 manufacture. The remaining 7 percent of cyclohexane consumed is used primarily as a solvent in low pressure polyethylene and as a plasticizer.

About 70 percent of cyclohexane is produced by the hydrogenation of benzene, and all new cyclohexane capacity is expected to use this route. The remainder is fractionated from natural gas liquids. A list of cyclohexane producers is shown in Table 1-4; this table also lists approximate benzene consumption in 1965.

TABLE 1-4—U.S. Cyclohexane Producers

Company	Location	Cyclo-hexane Capacity— millions of gallons/yr.	Estimated Benzene Consump- tion in 1965 millions of gallons/yr.[1]
Ashland	Catlettsburg, Ky.	20	15
Continental*	Ponca City, Okla.	40	30
DuPont	Belle, W. Va.	15	11
	Orange, Tex.	15	11
Gulf	Port Arthur, Tex.	30	22
Phillips	Borger, Tex.	30	0[2]
	Sweeny, Tex.	70	22[3]
Pontiac	Corpus Christi, Tex.	12	8
Atlantic-Richfield	Watson, Calif.	10	8
Signal	Houston, Tex.	12	9
South Hampton	Silsbee, Tex.	3	2
Union Oil	Smiths Bluff, Tex.	30	22
Total......................		287	160
Capacity to be added in 1966:			
Cosden	Big Spring, Tex.	8	
Enjay	Baytown, Tex.	18	
Eastman	Longview, Tex.	3	
Texaco	Port Arthur, Tex.	30	
Total......................		59	
Grand Total...............		346	

[1] Unless otherwise noted cyclohexane is produced by hydrogenation of benzene. In this process, 0.83 gallons of benzene are used per gallon of cyclohexane.
[2] All of cyclohexane fractionated from natural gas liquids.
[3] Part of cyclohexane fractionated from natural gas liquids.

* See Reference 5 at end of chapter.

Phenol. The consumption of U.S. phenol has shown a steady growth and this is expected to continue from now to 1970 at the rate of 5 percent a year; thus, phenol output should increase from an estimated 1,180 million pounds[7] in 1965 to 1,500 million pounds[7] in 1970. However, in terms of benzene consumption, phenol will only consume 19 percent of benzene in 1970 compared with 20 percent in 1965.

Phenolic Resins. The main consumer of phenol is phenolic resins; this outlet is expected to account for 50 percent of phenol consumption in 1965 and 54 percent in 1970. Phenolic resins are used in molding applications, adhesives, plywood bonding, laminating resins, friction materials, thermal insulation, and other miscellaneous applications.

Bisphenol A. Another important outlet for phenol is in bisphenol A; this material is expected to account for 8 percent of phenol consumption in 1965 and about the same in 1970. Bisphenol A's major outlet is in epoxies but polycarbonates should eventually account for a sizeable amount of bisphenol A consumption.

Alkyl Phenols. A third major outlet for phenol is in alkyl phenols, specifically nonyl phenol and dodecyl phenol. These materials will account for 7 percent of phenol consumption in 1965; they are used in nonionic and anionic surface-active agents, oil additives, rubber chemicals, and plastics. The detergent portion of this market will be small in 1970 because of the requirements of biodegradability. However, alkyl phenols will still account for about 5 percent of phenol consumption in 1970.

Others. The only other outlet accounting for over 5 percent of phenol consumption is caprolactam, which is used in the manufacture of Nylon 6. However, in this case phenol must compete with cyclohexane as a raw material and most of the future growth in caprolactam is

expected to be based on cyclohexane. By 1970 caprolactam should account for 6 percent of phenol consumption; this compares with 7 percent in 1965.

The other outlets for phenol are adipic acid, petroleum
refining, plasticizers, 2,4 D acids, salicylates, pentachlorophenol, export, and some additional miscellaneous uses.
Each of these markets consumes less than 5 percent of
total phenol produced and this is expected to still be the
case in 1970.

There are a number of different process routes to
phenol, but all of the important ones are based on benzene as a raw material. The route that has been used by
most of the recent expansions and is expected to be used
almost exclusively in the next five years is the cumene
route. In this process benzene is alkylated with propylene
to give cumene. Cumene in turn is oxidized and the
hydroperoxide is cleaved from the molecule resulting in
phenol and acetone. Other important process routes are:
(1) Chlorobenzene with caustic soda as a hydrolysis
agent, (2) benzene sulfonation, and (3) Raschig process
which utilizes HCl. Phenol is also made from toluene, but
this route accounts for less than 4 percent of total phenol
production.

A list of phenol producers is shown in Table 1-5, this
table also lists approximate benzene consumption in 1965.
Cumene producers are listed in Table 1-6.

Other Uses. Each of the remaining markets for benzene
accounts for less than 7 percent of total benzene consumption and this is expected to be the case in 1970.
These other markets for benzene are: (1) Detergent alkylate, which may be faced with severe competition from
alcohols several years from now, (2) aniline, which could
grow because of additional use in analine-based isocyanate
rigid foams, (3) maleic anhydride, which has a major
outlet in polyester resins, (4) DDT, whose market is not
expected to grow, and (5) exports, which are expected to

TABLE 1-5—U.S. Phenol Producers—Synthetic

Company	Location	Process	Phenol Capacity— millions of pounds/yr.	Estimated Benzene Consumption in 1965 —millions of gallons[1]
Allied*	Philadelphia, Pa.	Cumene	200	28[2]
Chevron	Richmond, Calif.	Cumene	50	7
Clark Oil	Chicago, Ill.	Cumene	30	4
Dow	Kalama, Wash.	Toluene	40	....
	Midland, Mich.	Chloro-benzene	230	28
Hercules*	Gibbstown, N.J.	Cumene	30	4
Hooker	South Shore, Ky.	Modified Raschig	65	8
	Tonawanda, N.Y.	Modified Raschig	65	8
Monsanto	Alvin, Tex.	Cumene	140	20
	Monsanto, Ill.	Sulfonation	115	14
Reichhold	Tuscaloosa, Ala.	Sulfonation	90	11
Schenectady	Rotterdam Jct., N.Y.	Benzene Oxidation	20	3
Shell	Houston, Tex.	Cumene	50	7
Skelly	Eldorado, Kan.	Cumene	50	7
Union Carbide	Marietta, Ohio	Modified Raschig	110	13
Total—Synthetic............			1285	162
Natural Phenol—Total............			60	
GRAND TOTAL—NATURAL and SYNTHETIC............			1345	
Capacity to be added in 1966:				
Allied	Philadelphia, Pa.	Cumene	100	
Union Carbide	Bound Brook, N.J.	Cumene	150	
Total to be added in 1966 =............			250	

[1] Pounds of benzene per pound of phenol are as follows for each process route:
Chlorobenzene..........1.18
Cumene...............1.16
Modified Raschig........1.1
Sulfonation.............1.0

[2] Allied purchases cumene from Gulf and Texaco; thus these latter two companies actually consume the benzene.

* See Reference 5 at end of chapter.

TABLE 1-6—U.S. Cumene Producers

Company	Location	Cumene Capacity— millions of pounds/yr.	Estimated Benzene Consumption in 1965 millions of gallons[1]
Amoco	Texas City, Tex.	50	0
Chevron	Richmond, Calif.	80	7
Clark*	Chicago, Ill.	50	4
Dow	Midland, Mich.	10	1
Gulf	Philadelphia, Pa.	180	17
Hercules*	Gibbstown, N.J.	50	4
Monsanto	Alvin, Tex.	240	20
Shell	Houston, Tex.	80	7
Skelly	El Dorado, Kan.	80	7
Texaco	Westville, N.J.	120	11
Total....................		935	78

Capacity to be added in 1966:
Plans have not been announced but some 400 million pounds/year of additional capacity will be required for new cumene-based phenol plants on the East Coast.
[1] Pounds of benzene used per pound of cumene = 0.685.

* See Reference 5 at end of chapter.

be virtually zero by 1970. This loss of the export market will be caused by the large-scale naphtha cracking units being constructed in Europe, with low-cost naphtha as a feedstock.

Lists of the producers of these chemicals which are minor outlets for benzene are shown in Tables 1-7, 1-8, 1-9 and 1-10, these tables also list approximate benzene consumption in 1965.

INDIVIDUAL COMPANIES

Table 1-11 shows the major sellers and buyers of benzene in the U.S. These are approximations based partially

TABLE 1-7—U.S. Detergent Alkylate Producers

Company	Location	Detergent Alkylate Capacity— millions of pounds/yr.	Estimated Benzene Consumption in 1965 —millions of gallons[1]
Allied	Buffalo, N.Y.	20	1
	North Claymont, Del.	100	3
Atlantic- Richfield	Port Arthur Tex.	100	3
Chevron	Richmond, Calif.	150	4
Continental	Baltimore, Md.	150	5
Monsanto	East St. Louis, Ill.	150	5
Phillips	Pasadena, Tex.	30	1
Union Carbide	Institute, W. Va.	150	5
Witfield	Watson, Calif.	30	1
Total		880	28

[1] Pounds of benzene used per pound of alkylate = 0.45.

on a review of published data and partially on the author's estimates.

This table shows that Shell is the number one benzene producer in the United States with a production of 96 million gallons/year followed by Enjay at 79 million gallons, Monsanto at 65, Gulf at 59, and Dow at 50 million gallons per year.

Dow is the number one consumer of benzene, with 1965 consumption estimated at 118 million gallons; Monsanto is a close second at 107, Union Carbide third at 63, and Gulf next with 39 million gallons.

Because of internal use of benzene, the amounts actually sold or purchased vary greatly from the amounts made or consumed. For example, Enjay is the largest seller, followed by Shell, Hess and Mobil. Dow is the

TABLE 1-8—U.S. Aniline Producers

Company	Location	Aniline Capacity— millions of pounds/yr.	Estimated Benzene Consumption in 1965 —millions of gallons[1]
Allied	Moundsville, W. Va.	40	4
American Cyanamid	Bound Brook, N. J.	60	5
	Willow Island, W. Va.	40	4
Dow	Midland, Mich.	25	2[1]
DuPont	Gibbstown, N.J.	85	7
Rubicon	Geismar, La.	35	1[2]
Total		285	23

[1] Dow uses chlorobenzene process (1.3 lbs. of benzene per pound of aniline); all others use nitrobenzene process (0.88 lbs. of benzene per pound of aniline).
[2] Starting up late in 1965.

largest buyer followed by Union Carbide, Monsanto, and DuPont.

Because of the large number of sellers and buyers, and because benzene can be transported easily, no one company can dominate the benzene market.

HISTORICAL DATA

Table 1-12 presents data based on U.S. Tariff Commission reports for 1953 through 1964 and on the author's estimates for 1965 and 1970.

These data show a gradual increase in U.S. total benzene production. The increase is due to the benzene produced by petroleum refiners as the benzene quantity produced by tar distillers and coke-oven operators has gradually declined. This is shown in Figure 1-7.

TABLE 1-9—U.S. Maleic Anhydride Producers

Company	Location	Maleic Anhydride Capacity— millions of pounds/yr.	Estimated Benzene Consumption in 1965 —millions of gallons[1]
Allied	Moundsville, W. Va.	20	2
Chevron	Richmond, Calif.	20	2
Koppers	Bridgeville, Pa.	20	2
Monsanto	East St. Louis, Ill.	60	7
Petro-Tex*	Houston, Tex.	20	0[1]
Pittsburgh Chemical	Neville Island, Pa.	20	2
Reichhold	Elizabeth, N.J.	20	2
Tenneco*	Fords, N. J.	12	1
Total		192	18

[1] All producers except Petro-Tex use oxidation of benzene (1.34 lbs. of benzene/lb. maleic anhydride), Petro-Tex uses butylenes as a raw material.

* See Reference 5 at end of chapter.

TABLE 1-10—U.S. DDT Producers

Company	Location	DDT Capacity— millions of pounds/yr.	Estimated Benzene Consumption in 1965 —millions of gallons[1]
Allied	Marcus Hook, Pa.	20	2
Diamond	Greens Bayou, Tex.	30	3
Geigy	McIntosh, Ala.	20	2
Lebanon	Lebanon, Pa.	15	1[2]
Montrose	Torrance, Calif.	75	6
Olin	Huntsville, Ala.	30	3
Total		190	17

[1] Pounds of benzene 1 lb. DDT = 0.86.
[2] Lebanon buys monochlorobenzene as a raw material; other companies on list buy it.

TABLE 1-11—Major Sellers and Buyers of Benzene
(Companies either selling or buying more than 10 million gallons of benzene in 1965)

COMPANY	BENZENE QUANTITY IN MILLION GALS/YR.			
	Use	Make	Sell	Buy
Enjay...................	0	79	79	..
Shell...................	30	96	66	..
Hess...................	0	30	30	..
Mobil..................	0	30	30	..
Bethlehem.............	0	26	26	..
U.S. Steel.............	2	28	26	..
Sunray-DX.............	0	22	22	..
Chevron...............	13	35	22	..
Suntide...............	4	25	21	..
Gulf...................	39	59	20	..
Texaco................	11	30	19	..
Crown Central.........	0	18	18	..
AtlanticRichfield......	9	27	18	..
Ashland...............	15	30	15	..
Sun...................	0	15	15	..
Tenneco...............	1	15	14	..
Republic Steel.........	0	12	12	..
Signal................	9	22	13	..
Atlas.................	0	10	10	..
Dow...................	118	50	..	68
Union Carbide.........	63	10	..	53
Monsanto..............	107	65	..	42
DuPont................	29	0	..	29
Conoco................	35	12	..	23
Sinclair-Koppers.......	22	0	..	22
Foster Grant..........	22	0	..	22
Hooker................	16	0	..	16
Reichhold.............	13	0	..	13

Average sales price has dropped gradually from 41 cents per gallon in 1953 to a low of 23 cents in 1963; this figure has recently increased and should average about 26 cents in 1965. Refer to Figure 1-8.

In spite of the increase in quantity of benzene produced the total annual sales value of benzene production hovered around the $100 million area from 1953 to 1959; it jumped to $174 million in 1961 only to drop back to $137 in 1962 under the impact of price drops. With firmer prices prevalent, sales value in 1965 should exceed the $200 million annual rate for the first time. Refer to Figure 1-9.

TABLE 1-12—Historical Data: U.S. Production, Number of Producers, and Sales Value of Benzene

Year	U.S. Production Millions gallons/yr.			No. of petro-leum opera-tors	Average sales value, ¢/gal., for all benzene sold	Value of total benzene production, millions dollars/yr.	Sales millions gal-lons/ yr.
	Total	Tar distillers and Coke-oven operators	Petro-leum opera-tors				
1953	273	210	63	17	41	91	234
1954	257	165	92	17	41	105	202
1955	308	209	99	16	37	114	265
1956	337	225	112	21	36	121	284
1957	331	215	116	18	35	116	277
1958	287	145	142	19	33	95	243
1959	347	138	209	21	29	100	331
1960	457	148	309	20	31	142	377
1961	545	132	413	30	32	174	421***
1962	546	128	418	30	25	137	405***
1963	647	121	526	32	23	149	421***
1964	738**	127**	611	30	22	162	465***
*1965	827	130	697	30	26	215	520
*1970	1150	130	1020	..	25–28	290–320	720

Source: U.S. Tariff Commission.
   * Estimates.
  ** Data reported by tar distillers not reported by Tariff Commission; tar distillers' production estimated at 8 million gallons.
 *** Tar distillers sales estimated to be negligible.

ECONOMICS

Only the economics of producing benzene from refinery reforming operations and from toluene will be discussed, as these two account for 80 percent of the U.S. benzene production and virtually all of the petrochemical benzene.

Benzene from Refinery Reformate. It is virtually impossible to determine an individual refiner's economics of producing benzene from reformate unless complete information is available on his gasoline pool quality compared with requirements, crude oil quality and price, existing processing equipment, and other variables. Since each refinery is different concerning these variables, it is possible only to make generalized remarks concerning

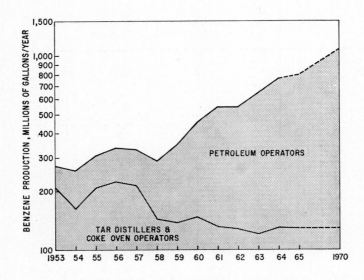

Figure 1-7. Peroleum operators have dominated the benzene market since 1958.

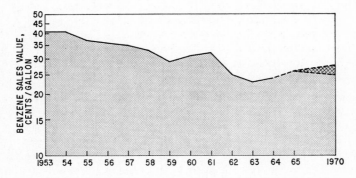

Figure 1-8. Sales price of benzene has shown a steady decline since 1953.

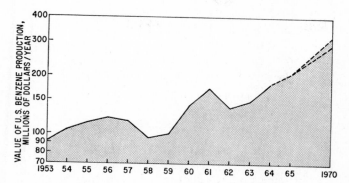

Figure 1-9. Value of U.S. benzene production has increased since 1953.

the economics of this operation. The major variable is the value of the benzene precursors in a refiner's gasoline pool—these precursors have a good octane value. This value of benzene precursors plus the necessary reforming plus solvent extraction and separation ordinarily result in a benzene value of 23 to 26 cents per gallon required for an acceptable return on investment. The reformer cost can vary widely depending on whether the refiner has an existing reformer running on C_7 and C_8's that can be incrementally expanded to run on C_6's or whether a new reformer must be built. The benzene value at which a refiner will dump benzene precursors into his gasoline pool rather than make benzene with equipment already installed is believed to be around 20 cents or slightly under.

Most U.S. refiners today have some reformer capacity already installed; therefore the economics of producing benzene and other aromatics versus using the straight-run gasoline from the crude distillation unit directly in the gasoline pool are not relevant in the United States; however, a recent study showed that payout time on a pretax basis varied from 1.85 years for 25-cent benzene, 21-cent toluene, and 25-cent xylene to 5.55 years for 21-cent benzene, 14.5-cent toluene, and 17-cent xylene.[1] It is worthwhile noting that benzene, toluene, and xylene are produced in about the following ratios in refineries:

$$\text{Benzene} = 1$$
$$\text{Toluene} = 2.5 \text{ to } 3.0$$
$$\text{Xylenes and Ethylbenzene} = 2.0 \text{ to } 2.5$$

These proportions vary from refinery to refinery; but it is obvious that the values of toluene, xylenes, and ethylbenzene play a major role in benzene profitability.

Benzene from Dealkylation of Toluene. In the case of benzene from toluene the economics can be approached by the traditional method of starting with a raw material cost and adding conversion costs and profit.

Sales values required to meet various financial objectives are shown in the following table.[2]

Basis: 15 million gallons of benzene/yr.

U.S. Gulf Coast location.	
Battery Limits Capital	= $1.5 million
or 10 cents/annual gal.	
Offsite Capital at 33% of B.L.	= $0.5 million
Total Capital	= $2.0 million
or 13.3 cents/annual gal.	

Direct Operating Costs = 2.3 cents a gallon
Return on Investment = 20% before tax
Sales and Administration Overhead = 1 cent/gallon

The table below shows the large effect toluene value has on required benzene sales prices (refer Figure 1-10).

The grand total represents the sales value required to justify a new plant; the out-of-pocket costs represent the sales value required to keep from shutting down an existing plant. Note the large effect toluene value has on required sales price.

	All figures in cents/gal.				
Toluene value	14	15	16	17	18
Raw material cost of benzene	17.5	18.8	20	21.2	22.5
Direct operating costs	2.3	2.3	2.3	2.3	2.3
Subtotal—Out of pocket costs	19.8	21.1	22.3	23.5	24.8
Depreciation at 10% of B.L. plant	1.0	1.0	1.0	1.0	1.0
Subtotal—Breakeven costs	20.8	22.1	23.3	24.5	25.8
Return on investment at 20%	2.7	2.7	2.7	2.7	2.7
Subtotal without sales & admin.	23.5	24.8	26.0	27.2	28.5
Sales & admin. overhead	1.0	1.0	1.0	1.0	1.0
Grand Total	24.5	25.8	27.0	28.2	29.5

Note: These figures assume hydrogen is valued at about $2\frac{1}{2}$ times fuel value. Although some refiners have hydrogen at fuel value now the large amounts of hydrogen to be required in the future in refineries for hydrocracking will result in hydrogen values higher than fuel value. Hydrogen taken at fuel value would decrease required benzene price by 0.8 cent per gallon.

Substantially more toluene is produced from benzene-toluene-xylene (BTX) operations than can be absorbed in the chemical and solvent markets; this excess toluene is dumped into gasoline. Therefore, the value of toluene will continue to be related closely to the price of gasoline and the requirements of octane for the nation's gasoline pool. Toluene has been reported as being sold for 14.5 to 17 cents per gallon in the recent past; thus a benzene sales price of 25 to 28 cents per gallon would be required to justify the construction of a new dealkylation plant. A larger capacity plant than 15 million gallons would result in a lower required benzene price although this has a small effect compared with variation in toluene price.

THE FUTURE

Consumption of benzene produced in the United States will continue to increase and an additional 350 million gallons will be required in 1970 over the 800 million gallons[4] required in 1965. The big uncertainty in this prediction is whether cyclohexane will continue to be exported in large quantities; if cyclohexane exports drop, U.S. benzene production in 1970 could be 100 million

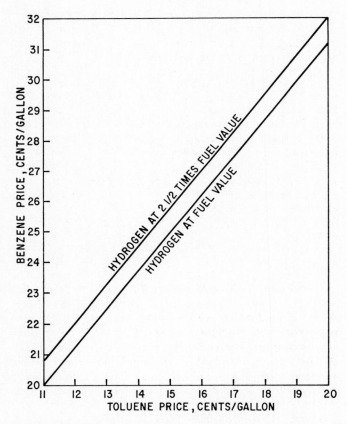

Figure 1-10. Gives benzene price required to earn 20 percent return on investment before taxes on dalkylation plant.

gallons lower than the above prediction. Even so, substantial quantities of benzene in excess of existing and announced capacity will be required.

The question that must be answered is: "From where will this additional benzene be obtained?" Benzene production from the steel and coal industries is limited by steel production rate and practices and is not expected to increase. Thus there seem to be four main sources of benzene for the future in the U.S.

1. **Benzene from Refinery Reformate.** Most of the refiners in the large petrochemical centers such as the Houston area are now producing benzene by this process; however, there are a number of large refineries in other parts of the United States that do not produce benzene. Undoubtedly some of these will do so in the future although it may take a benzene price at the same level required to justify dealkylation of toluene in order to induce some of these refiners to produce benzene; generally the existing large refiners that have not installed benzene manufacturing facilities do not have as good an economic base as the major Gulf Coast refiners because of type of crude oil and/or greater distance from the benzene markets.

2. **Benzene from Dealkylation of Toluene.** Unless large volumes of benzene are produced from naphtha crackers in the United States or Puerto Rico as discussed below, it appears that substantial quantities of benzene will be produced by the dealkylation of toluene. As indicated in the section on economics, a benzene price of 25 cents to 28 cents a gallon is required to induce a company to produce benzene by this route. Thus it seems very possible that benzene price in the United States over the next few years could remain in this range.

3. **Benzene from Naphtha Crackers in the United States or Puerto Rico.** Benzene along with ethylene, propylene, and other petrochemicals can be produced by cracking naphtha or other liquid hydrocarbons. The economics of this operation depend on two main items: The markets available for the wide spectrum of chemicals produced from a naphtha cracker and the price of

the naphtha raw material. Gasoline is the premium refinery product in the United States so naphtha has a relatively high value; thus only a few U.S. companies use liquid feedstock to make petrochemicals in large quantities: Enjay (naphtha and gas oil), Mobil (naphtha), and Monsanto (condensate). However, outside the U.S. naphtha is available at a much lower price. Several U.S. companies have asked for a Foreign Trade Zone to allow the production of petrochemicals in the United States with foreign-naphtha feed; others have requested permission to build petrochemical complexes in Puerto Rico and import the gasoline and petrochemicals into the United States.

The decision of the U.S. government on these two questions will play a major role in the future source of benzene raw material and in benzene price.[6] If the requests are granted benzene should be available at 25 cents or even a few cents less. If they are not granted then the price of benzene will be based on the economics of producing benzene from toluene.

4. Benzene From a Foreign Producing Area such as Europe. The quantity of benzene that might be imported from an area such as Europe is particularly difficult to foresee; it depends on the relative growth of the various segments of the entire petrochemical market in Europe, including ethylene, propylene, and other chemicals. Also the future U.S. tariff policy will have a major effect; at the present time there is no import duty on benzene. Nevertheless, large-scale importation of cheap foreign benzene could result in import duties.

Neglecting possibilities Numbers Three and Four above, it seems that toluene dealkylation will be a major source of additional capacity. Approximately 2.5 times as much toluene is made in an aromatics plant as is benzene. Since chemical markets do not exist for most of this toluene, the excess is dumped into the gasoline pool.

Therefore, the benzene price must be high enough to induce a company to keep toluene out of the gasoline pool and dealkylate it to benzene. Thus with benzene in the 25-cent to 28-cent price range, there should be ample quantities of it available to meet U.S. needs for a number of years.

With benzene in this price range and with an annual production of 1,150 million gallons, the value of benzene produced in the United States in 1970 should approximate $300 million. Refer to Figure 1-9.

Literature Cited

1. Jenkins, Jerry G., "How Cosden Makes Polystyrene from Crude Oil," *The Oil and Gas Journal*, 63, No. 3, p. 78-86 (Jan. 18, 1965).

2. Calculated by author from data presented in: Asselin, G. F. and R. A. Erickson, "Benzene and Naphthalene from Petroleum by the Hydeal Process," *Chemical Engineering Progress*, 58, No. 4, p. 47-52 (April 1962).

3. Sources such as *Hydrocarbon Processing & Petroleum Refiner; Oil, Paint and Drug Reporter; Chemical Engineering; Oil and Gas Journal; Chemical Week;* and *Chemical and Engineering News* were used for news items and market and capacity estimates. Final estimates published, however, represent the best estimates of the author who takes full responsibility for them.

4. Tariff Commission preliminary reports show 1965 production as 827 million gallons. Table 1-12 has been revised accordingly.

5. These companies have added or are adding additional capacity as of mid-1966.

6. See Reference 1, Chapter 5.

7. Refer to Chapters 2, 3, and 4 for revised estimates and more detail.

2

Cyclohexane

BENZENE-HYDROGENATION PLANTS account for 70 percent of U.S. cyclohexane and will provide an even greater percentage in the future. Consumption of U.S. cyclohexane is expected to grow 13 percent a year between 1965 and 1970, thus resulting in a 1970 demand of 460 million gallons versus 250 million gallons[9] in 1965. Export sales represent the largest single outlet for cyclohexane in 1965, with Nylon 66 intermediates the next largest. By 1970, the consumption of cyclohexane in Nylon 66 intermediates will equal or surpass the export market. Cyclohexane is also used as a raw material for Nylon 6; non-nylon uses are very small.

Cyclohexane price in the next few years should remain the same as benzene, that is, remain in the 25-cent to 28-cent a gallon range; benzene and hydrogen values are the two main determinants of cyclohexane cost. Hydrogen is becoming more valuable to refiners and eventually cyclohexane will be worth a slight premium over the benzene price/gallon. The total value of cyclohexane produced in the United States is $65 million in 1965 and will pass the $100 million mark before 1970. The largest unknown facing the U.S. cyclohexane business is the extent to which foreign markets are available in the future.

MANUFACTURE

Cyclohexane is obtained from two main sources:

Hydrogenation of benzene	70 percent
Fractionation from petroleum streams	30 percent
	100 percent

Phillips is the only company that obtains cyclohexane by the fractionation of petroleum streams although in the past other companies including Humble, Shell, and Richfield used this route. Originally these companies produced a stream with a purity of 85 percent, but with increased competition of the 99⁺ percent purity from benzene hydrogenation units the 85 percent material could no longer be sold at a worthwhile price to fiber manufacturers. With additional processing, believed to include the isomerization of methylcyclopentane to cyclohexane, Phillips today produces a cyclohexane almost comparable in purity to that produced by the benzene-hydrogenation processors.

It is believed that Phillips has reached the end of available feedstock from which to recover cyclohexane, as a recent expansion at Phillips' Sweeny complex included a benzene-hydrogenation unit. It is doubtful that any other company will have available a sufficiently large pool of naphthenic material from which to recover cyclohexane commercially; therefore, all future expansion is expected to be based on the benzene-hydrogenation route. This route should account for 84 percent of U.S. cyclohexane by 1970.

The chemistry of production of cyclohexane by the isomerization of methylcyclopentane is shown in Figure 2-1. Details of Phillips' fractionation scheme have not

METHYLCYCLOPENTANE ──────► CYCLOHEXANE

$C_5H_9CH_3$ ──────────► C_6H_{12}

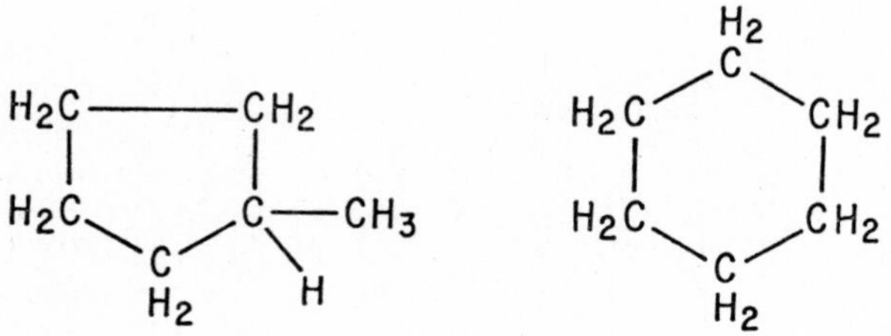

Figure 2-1. Chemistry of isomerizing methylcyclopentane to cyclohexane.

been published. The details of the benzene-hydrogenation route are given below.

Benzene-Hydrogenation Route to Cyclohexane. It is believed that all of U.S. producers except DuPont use a vapor-phase hydrogenation process; DuPont uses a liquid-phase process. A popular process in the United States has been U.O.P.'s Hydrar process, which is shown in Figure 2-2. In this process the benzene feed, recycle cyclohexane, and fresh and recycle hydrogen are brought to reaction temperature and charged to the reactor. The conversion of benzene to cyclohexane is stoichiometric. After leaving the reactor the effluent enters a heat exchanger and then a separator. Gas from the separator is recycled to the reactor. A portion of the cyclohexane removed from the separator is recycled to the reactor to assist in controlling the reactor temperature. The product cyclohexane is flashed to remove light hydrocarbons.

Institute Francais du Petrole offers a process, shown in Figure 2-3; the economics of this process have been

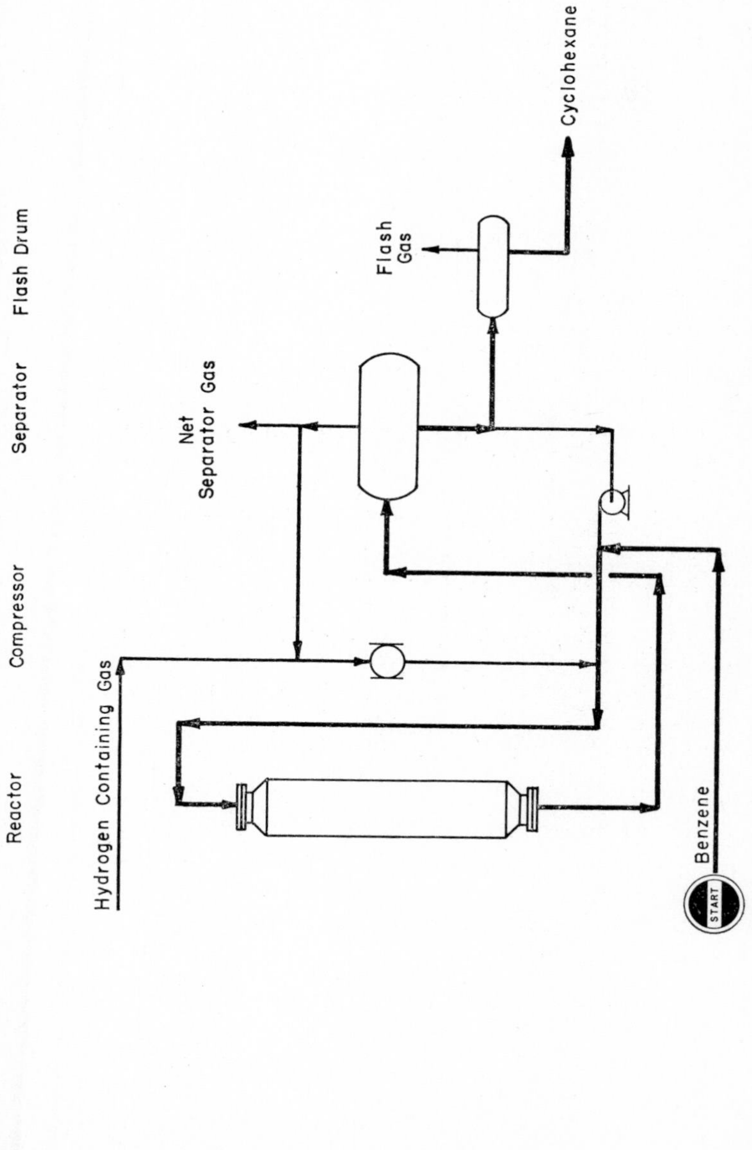

Figure 2-2. Cyclohexane by benzene hydrogenation using U.O.P.'s Hydrar process.

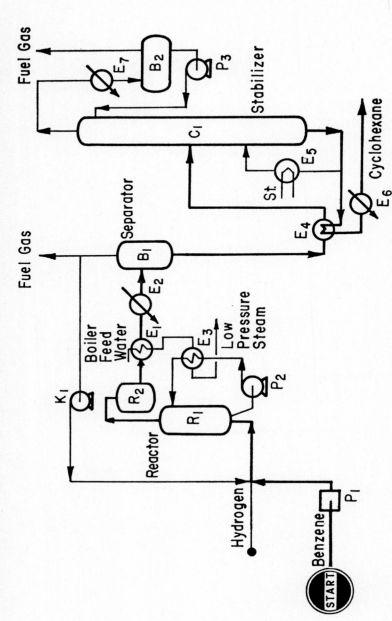

Figure 2-3. Benzene can be hydrogenated to cyclohexane in this I.F.P. process.

published and are discussed in detail in the section entitled Economics.

The chemistry of producing cyclohexane by hydrogenation of benzene is shown in Figure 2-4. Note that three moles of hydrogen are required for each mol of cyclohexane produced.

BENZENE + HYDROGEN ⟶ CYCLOHEXANE

$$C_6H_6 \quad + \quad 3H_2 \quad \longrightarrow \quad C_6H_{12}$$

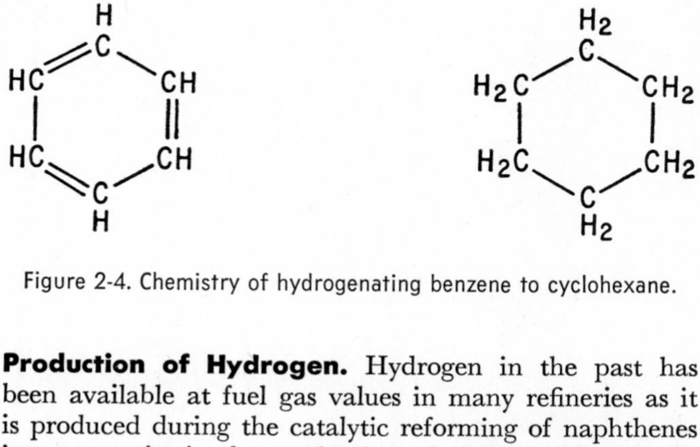

Figure 2-4. Chemistry of hydrogenating benzene to cyclohexane.

Production of Hydrogen. Hydrogen in the past has been available at fuel gas values in many refineries as it is produced during the catalytic reforming of naphthenes into aromatics in the production of gasoline. Fortunately this hydrogen is available at a purity and pressure satisfactory for use in cyclohexane manufacture. However, between 1960 and 1965 the amount of refinery hydrogen burned as fuel dropped from about 50 percent of the total available down to 25 percent because of increased usage of hydrogen in hydrotreating, hydrocracking, and cyclohexane manufacture. In the future the growth of hydrocracking will cause a general shortage of hydrogen in the refineries and more refiners will have to manufacture hydrogen deliberately. There are various processes avail-

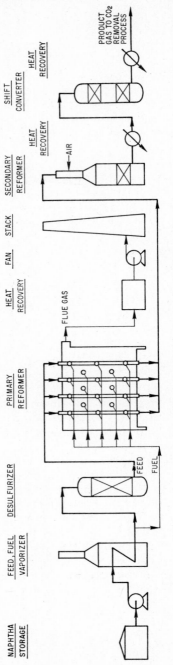

Figure 2.5. Manufacture of hydrogen by naphtha reforming.

able for the manufacture of hydrogen; a variety of feedstocks can be used, including natural gas and naphtha.
The process shown in Figure 2-5 can be used with either
natural gas or a naphtha feedstock. In the Gulf Coast
area, natural gas is the preferred feedstock, while in
overseas locations naphtha may be used.

Another source of hydrogen is some of the waste gas
streams in refineries and chemical plants; either a cryo-
genic process or a palladium-diffusion purification process
can be used to recover this hydrogen depending on the
purities and volumes of the waste gas available. Union
Carbide recently introduced the new palladium-diffusion
process and nine plants are in operation in 1965. The
flow plan for this process is shown in Figure 2-6.

The economics of cyclohexane production, including
the influence of hydrogen costs, are discussed in a separate
section.

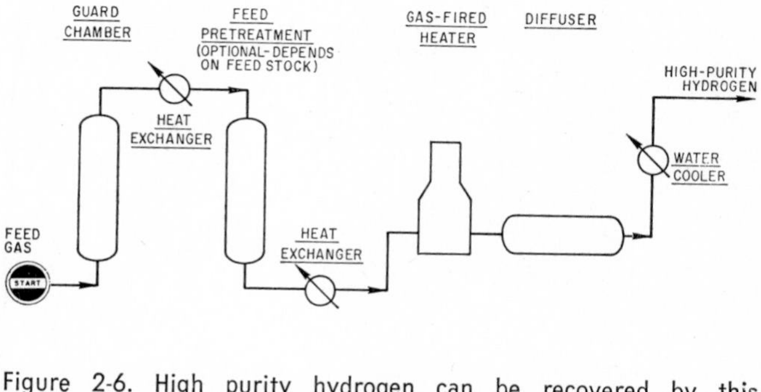

Figure 2-6. High purity hydrogen can be recovered by this
palladium diffusion process.[7]

U.S. Cyclohexane Producers. These are listed in
Table 2-1.

TABLE 2-1—U.S. Cyclohexane Producers

Company	Location	Cyclohexane Capacity— Millions of Gallons/Yr.
Ashland....................	Catlettsburg, Ky.	20
Continental...............	Ponca City, Okla.	40
DuPont....................	Belle, W. Va.	15*
	Orange, Tex.	15
Gulf......................	Port Arthur, Tex.	30
Phillips...................	Borger, Tex.	30
	Sweeny, Tex.	45
		25
Pontiac...................	Corpus Christi, Tex.	12
Richfield..................	Watson, Calif.	10
Signal....................	Houston, Tex.	12
South Hampton............	Silsbee, Tex.	3
Union Oil.................	Smiths Bluff, Tex.	30
Total............	....	287
Capacity to be added in 1966:		
Cosden....................	Big Spring, Tex.	8
Enjay.....................	Baytown, Tex.	18
Eastman...................	Longview, Tex.	3
Texaco....................	Port Arthur, Tex.	30
Total...		59
Grand Total...		346

* This plant is rumored to be shut down.

MARKETS

The markets for U.S. cyclohexane are projected to grow about 13 percent a year over the next five years, from an estimated 250 million gallons[9] in 1965 to 460 million gallons in 1970. Refer to Table 2-2 and Figure 2-7.

This projected growth in cyclohexane markets is dependent on the ability of the U.S. producers to continue to export large quantities of cyclohexane. Also it is dependent on cyclohexane routes to Nylon 6 and Nylon 66 remaining competitive with alternate routes; this in turn is affected by the research, engineering, and manufacturing functions of the various companies in addition to the aggressiveness of the various companies involved in the nylon race. Cyclohexane is used primarily in adipic acid, which is used to make Nylon 66, and in caprolactam,

TABLE 2-2—Markets for U.S. Cyclohexane—1965 and 1970

	Millions of Gallons	
	1965	1970
Export...	112	198*
Nylon 66 intermediates (mostly adipic acid)...	103	198
Caprolactam for nylon 6.......................	18	36
Non-Nylon uses.................................	14	23
Adipic acid for non-nylon uses...............	3	5
Total...................................	250[9]	460
	1965	1970
Subtotals: Non-nylon	17	28
U.S. nylon	121	234

* This estimate subject to high degree of uncertainty.

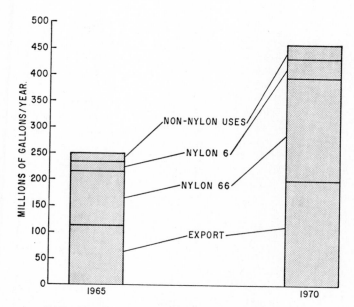

Figure 2-7. These are the markets for U.S. cyclohexane.

which is used to make Nylon 6. These items will be discussed in more detail below.

Nylon Markets. Between 1954 and 1964 nylon markets in the United States grew at an average annual rate of some 35 percent; at present they are growing at the rate of 15 percent a year and are expected to continue a growth rate of 10 to 15 percent a year for the next five years. Total nylon production in 1965 is expected to be about 880 million pounds;[11] filament yarn will account for 780 million pounds, staple fibers 55 million pounds, and casting resins 45 million pounds. A breakdown of 1965 consumption of nylon is shown in Table 2-3. Approxi-

TABLE 2-3—U.S. Nylon Consumption

	Millions of Pounds 1965
Filament Yarn:	
Tire Cords...............	250
Apparel..................	160
Carpets, rugs............	130
Industrial...............	80
Hosiery..................	50
Upholstery..............	50
Other (including exports).....	60
Subtotal filament yarn.......	780
Staple Fiber....................	55
Casting Resins.................	45
Total......................	880[11]

mately 80 percent of total output is Nylon 66. By 1970, over-all U.S. production of nylon is expected to be near 1,500 million pounds; there are several reasons for such a rapid growth:

1. DuPont and Monsanto have been the only producers of Nylon 66; they are now being joined by Fiber Industries (62.5 percent Celanese and 37.5 percent I.C.I.) and Beaunit-El Paso. These two newcomers are expected to be aggressive and increased competition and probable lowering of prices should result in increased consumption.

Previous studies have shown that although there is

not a good correlation between number of producers and price changes, that an increase in number of producers along with increased annual production is usually accompanied by substantially lower prices when considering a long period of time.[1]

Nylon prices have begun to fall in recent years; in June, 1964, the price of heavy denier bulked continuous filament nylon carpet yard dropped from $1.53 to $1.21 a pound, or a drop of 21 percent! More recently, in June, 1965, the price of heavy denier Nylon 6 and Nylon 66 yarns used for industrial purposes were cut 11 percent.

2. Nylon holds three-fourths of the market for tire cords for replacement passenger car tires but has managed to get less than 3 percent of the original equipment automobile tire market. This lack of penetration into the "original equipment" market has been due to "flat-spotting", which causes a rough ride the first few miles after the tires have been sitting idle. Much development work has gone into improving Nylon 66 and Nylon 6 so as to reduce or prevent flat-spotting. DuPont has introduced a Nylon N-44 that supposedly does not flat-spot but yet offers greater strength over rayon tire cords; however, the producers of rayon tire cords claim N-44 has no important advantages. However, with rayon enjoying 96 percent of the original-equipment passenger-car market, there is a good possibility of substantially increased nylon sales. There are long-range developments such as radial-ply tires which may favor polyester, glass, or steel as a tire-cord material; however, these developments are not expected to affect nylon tire cord sales in the years just ahead.

3. A larger number of U.S. residents are moving into apartments and most new apartments have wall-to-wall carpeting. Nylon is popular in this market because of its durability. Additionally, carpeting is making inroads into schools, hospitals, and office buildings. That there is much room for growth in these markets is exemplified by the fact that many offices of some of the nylon makers are still not carpeted!

4. The small-denier textured nylon yarn, which is commonly referred to as "stretch nylon," now accounts for 50 percent of the apparel outlet for nylon. The market for this material has been growing 40 to 50 percent a year.

Nylon 66 Versus Nylon 6. Nylon 66 holds about 80 percent of the U.S. market for nylon fiber; on the other hand, Nylon 6 is the dominant fiber in Europe. In the early 1960s, there was considerable sentiment to the effect that Nylon 6 would gradually capture many of the markets in the U.S. held by Nylon 66; this sentiment existed because it was felt that Nylon 6 was as good a performer as Nylon 66 and either was or would be cheaper to make. To date, Nylon 66 has resisted the inroads of Nylon 6 and continues to remain by far the dominant nylon fiber in the United States. It is significant that Beaunit, which makes Nylon 6 fiber, has decided to enter the Nylon 66 business while none of the Nylon 66 manufacturers have decided to start making Nylon 6.

Nylon 66 has higher strength, higher modulus, greater resistance to oxidation, and a higher melting point than Nylon 6; these properties give Nylon 66 a better opportunity for wider usage. Nylon 6 has been popular in Europe because it was originally developed there and the knowhow was more readily available.

Routes to Nylon 66. Nylon 66 is formed by the condensation of hexamethylenediamine (HMDA) with adipic acid. All of the adipic acid used in nylon manufacture is obtained from cyclohexane; however, HMDA is made a variety of ways, one of which starts with adipic acid as a raw material. Thus, depending on the process route selected for HMDA, varying amounts of cyclohexane are required per pound of Nylon 66. The diagrams below indicate the routes selected by the companies making or planning to make Nylon 66.

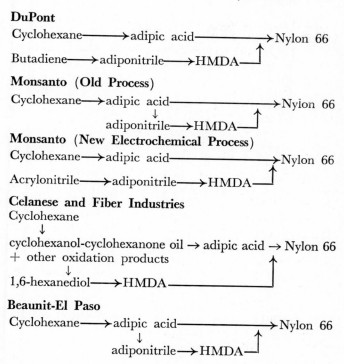

DuPont

Cyclohexane———→adipic acid————————→Nylon 66

Butadiene———→adiponitrile———→HMDA——⌐

Monsanto (Old Process)

Cyclohexane———→adipic acid————————→Nylon 66
                      ↓
              adiponitrile———→HMDA——⌐

Monsanto (New Electrochemical Process)

Cyclohexane———→adipic acid————————→Nylon 66

Acrylonitrile———→adiponitrile———→HMDA——⌐

Celanese and Fiber Industries

Cyclohexane
     ↓
cyclohexanol-cyclohexanone oil → adipic acid → Nylon 66
+ other oxidation products
     ↓
1,6-hexanediol———→HMDA————————⌐

Beaunit-El Paso

Cyclohexane———→adipic acid————————→Nylon 66
                      ↓
              adiponitrile———→HMDA——⌐

Note that Monsanto's old process, Celanese's process, and Beaunit-El Paso's process use cyclohexane as the starting material for both the adipic acid and HMDA; thus Nylon 66 made by these processes consumes twice as much cyclohexane per pound of nylon as the DuPont process or Monsanto's electrochemical process. Therefore, the future growth of cyclohexane consumption will be affected by the relative success of Fiber Industries and Beaunit-El Paso compared with DuPont and Monsanto. Also affecting cyclohexane consumption will be the degree of success realized by Monsanto's new electrochemical process; a plant using this process was placed onstream in mid-1965 but as yet no details of commercial operation are available. It is believed that this new plant will cater to the growth in Monsanto's nylon business and that the old plant will also remain in service.

Routes to Nylon 6. Nylon 6 is obtained by the polycondensation of caprolactam. There are at least five different process routes to caprolactam; four of these start with cyclohexane and the fifth starts with phenol as a raw material. In the United States, Allied uses the phenol process while the other two manufacturers use a cyclohexane route. Little has been published about the relative merits and economics of the various routes to caprolactam; nevertheless, indications are that one of the cyclohexane routes is better than the phenol route as BASF in Germany switched from phenol to cyclohexane in 1963 and Bayer added a caprolactam plant based on cyclohexane in 1964 although it had an existing plant based on phenol. On the other hand, there has been no indication that Allied will switch its U.S. plant to cyclohexane; should such an event take place it would make a strong impact on cyclohexane usage.

Although little has been published about the yields or costs of the various cyclohexane routes to caprolactam, both the Toyo Rayon and the Union Carbide route are thought to have a manufacturing cost of 20¢/pound or less; this compares with a posted price in the *Oil, Paint and Drug Reporter* in mid-1965 of 41¢/pound and an average price of 37¢/pound realized from sales in the United States in 1963 (U.S. Tariff Commission report). The Toyo Rayon route is reported to use slightly less than 1.0 pound of cyclohexane per pound of caprolactam.

Thus cyclohexane consumption in the Nylon 6 market depends on how well the other U.S. makers fare against Allied, on whether or not Allied switches to a cyclohex-

ane-based route, and on the yields of the various cyclohexane routes used.

Cyclohexane Markets: Exports. Export sales will account for approximately 112 million gallons of cyclohexane sales in 1965, or about 45 percent of total U.S. production of cyclohexane. Most of the cyclohexane which is exported is used to make caprolactam, which in turn is used to make Nylon 6 fiber. Europe represents by far the largest export market.

This export market has grown very rapidly—as recently as 1961 it was only 25 million gallons a year. It is not expected to grow as rapidly in the years ahead as it has in the recent past; however, many market authorities expect a continued growth. If the export market grows at a 12 percent annual rate between 1965 and 1970 then 1970 exports will be 198 million pounds (Table 2-2 and Figure 2-7).

Even though the market experts are predicting a rise in exports, the true picture is less certain. There is a large buildup of cyclohexane plants starting overseas and the foreign capacities are expected to double from 1965 to 1966—from 100 million gallons in 1965 to 200 million gallons in 1966. Depending on the outcome of the requests for Foreign-Trade Zones in the United States and requests for quotas enabling petrochemical complexes to be built in Puerto Rico, it is possible that 1970 exports will be smaller than those in 1965. If this should happen the growth of cyclohexane production in the United States would slow drastically. Undoubtedly manufacturers and prospective manufacturers of cyclohexane are watching the exports picture very closely.

Cyclohexane Markets: Adipic Acid and Other Nylon Intermediates. It is estimated that about 106 million gallons of cyclohexane will be consumed in the manufacture of adipic acid in 1965; this represents 42 percent of U.S. cyclohexane production. Some 97 percent of the adipic acid made from cyclohexane is used to make Nylon 66; the remainder of the adipic acid made from cyclohexane and the adipic acid made from phenol is used as a plasticizer, in the manufacture of urethane foams and elastomers, and in the food industry.

The U.S. adipic acid producers are listed in Table 2-4. The capacities shown for the various companies do not check with those normally published for adipic acid producers; nevertheless, based on reported production of adipic acid by the U.S. Tariff Commission these capacities are believed to be approximately correct.

U.S. Nylon 66 fiber producers are listed in Table 2-5.

As indicated above under Routes to Nylon 66, the growth in adipic acid consumption will depend on the relative success of Fiber Industries and Beaunit-El Paso compared with DuPont and Monsanto and on the commercial success of Monsanto's new electrochemical process. Table 2-2 shows cyclohexane consumption in adipic acid and other Nylon 66 intermediates growing at the rate of 14 percent annually to a total of 198 million pounds in 1970; note that this includes all of the cyclohexane to be used by Celanese (for Fiber Industries) even though it is believed that part of this cyclohexane will be converted to HMDA without actually going through the adipic acid stage.

Adipic acid is made from cyclohexane by a two-step oxidation process in which cyclohexane is first oxidized to cyclohexanol-cyclohexanone; this step is followed by a nitric acid oxidation to adipic acid. An alternate route is via a one-step oxidation.

Cyclohexane Markets: Caprolactam. Caprolactam manufacture in the United States is expected to consume only 18 million gallons of cyclohexane in 1965, or about 7 percent of U.S. production. This share of total cyclo-

TABLE 2-4—U.S. Adipic Producers

Company	Location	Adipic Acid Capacity— Millions of Pounds/Yr.	Estimated Cyclohexane Consumption in 1965— Millions of Gallons*
Allied............	Hopewell, Va.	20	0*
Celanese[10]........	Bay City, Tex.	35	4
DuPont[10].........	Belle, W. Va.	210	25
DuPont[10].........	Orange, Tex.	210	25
Monsanto[10].......	Luling, La.	30	0*
Monsanto[10].......	Pensacola, Fla.	405	49
Rohm & Haas.....	Louisville, Ky.	20	3
Total........		930	106

Additional capacity announced:			
Beaunit-El Paso[10]..	Odessa, Tex.	40 (Complete by 1966)	
Celanese...........	Bay City, Tex.	35 (Complete by 1967)	
DuPont...........	Victoria, Tex.	.. (Complete by 1968)	

*All plants except Allied at Hopewell and Monsanto at Luling start with cyclohexane as a raw material; these two plants use phenol as a raw material. In the cyclohexane process, 0.12 gallons of cyclohexane are assumed to be used per pound of adipic acid.

TABLE 2-5—U.S. Nylon 66 Producers (Fiber)

Company	Location	Nylon 66 Capacity— Millions of pounds/yr.	
DuPont[10]..............	Chattanooga, Tenn.	90	
	Martinsville, Va.	90	
	Richmond, Va.	150	
	Seaford, Del.	70	
	Company Total		400
Fiber Industries*......	Greenville, S.C.		40
Monsanto.............	Greenwood, S.C.	25	
	Pensacola, Fla.	175	
	Company Total		200
Total...............			640
Announced additions:			
Beaunit-El Paso.......	TVA Vicinity	40 (startup date: 1966)	

* Fiber Industries is owned 62.5% by Celanese and 37.5% by I.C.I.

TABLE 2-6—U.S. Caprolactam Producers

Company	Location	Caprolactam Capacity— Millions of Pounds/Yr.	Estimated Cyclohexane Consumption in 1965— Millions of Gallons*
Allied[10]............	Hopewell, Va.	140	0
Dow Badische[10].....	Freeport, Tex.	60	10
DuPont.............	Beaumont, Tex.	50	8
Total..........		250	18

Announced expansions:
Columbia Nipro Corporation (50% Pittsburgh Plate Glass and 50% Dutch State Mines) have announced a 44 million pound/yr. plant at Augusta, Ga.; will probably use cyclohexane as a raw material.

*Allied uses phenol as a starting raw material; the other two use cyclohexane. In the cyclohexane process, 0.16 gallons of cyclohexane are assumed to be used per pound of caprolactam.

hexane market is smaller than usually reported, but it is based on estimated total U.S. carpolactam manufacture and the fact that Allied, the largest manufacturer of caprolactam, uses phenol as a raw material.

Cyclohexane consumption is expected to double to 36 million gallons annually by 1970, with virtually all being used in Nylon 6.

U.S. caprolactam producers are listed in Table 2-6. U.S. Nylon 6 fiber producers are listed in Table 2-7.

Caprolactam can be made from cyclohexane by at least four different processes: (1) The Iventa A.G. process in which cyclohexane is oxidized to cyclohexanol and cyclohexanone, which is converted to cyclohexanone oxime, and finally to caprolactam; (2) the DuPont route in which cyclohexane is converted to nitrocyclohexane, next to cyclohexanone oxime, which is converted to caprolactam; (3) the Toyo Rayon process in which cyclohexane is reacted with nitrosyl chloride to give cyclohexanone oxime, which is converted to caprolactam; and (4) the Union Carbide route in which cyclohexane is oxidized and dehydrogenated to cyclohexanone, which is oxidized to caprolactone, which is converted to caprolactam. The

TABLE 2-7—U.S. Nylon 6 Producers (Fiber)

Company	Location	Nylon 6 Capacity—Millions of Pounds/Yr.
Allied........................	Columbia, S. C.	43
American Enka................	Hopewell, Va.	100
	Enka, N.C.	45
Beaunit[10]....................	Lowland, Tenn.	35
Firestone[10]....................	Elizabethton, Tenn.	4
Courtaulds....................	Hopewell, Va.	30
	LeMoyne, Ala.	20
Total.....................		277

Announced expansions:
American Enka is expanding at Enka, N. C., and Lowland, Tenn., to a total Nylon 6 capacity of 90 million pounds/yr.

relative economics and yields of the processes are not available.

Cyclohexane Markets: Non-Nylon. It is estimated that 14 million gallons of cyclohexane will be used for non-nylon markets in the U.S. in 1965; this is equivalent to about 6 percent of total U.S. production. These markets should grow to 23 million pounds by 1970 and thus account for 5 percent of total U.S. cyclohexane production. (These figures exclude the cyclohexane used to make adipic acid for non-nylon purposes.)

In the non-nylon markets, cyclohexane is used as a solvent in the manufacture of Phillips-type high density polyethylene and as a raw material in the manufacture of cyclohexanol and cyclohexanone; a possible large volume outlet in the future will be phenol as a process has been developed using cyclohexane as a raw material.

INDIVIDUAL COMPANIES

Table 2-8 shows U.S. major sellers and buyers of cyclohexane. These are approximations based partially

TABLE 2-8—Major Sellers and Buyers of Cyclohexane
(Companies either selling or buying 10 million gallons or more of cyclohexane in 1965. Export sellers are included; export buyers are excluded.)

COMPANY	CYCLOHEXANE QUANTITY IN MILLIONS GALS/YR.			
	USE	MAKE	SELL	BUY
Phillips.......................	0	100	100	..
Continental................	0	40	40	..
Union (formerly Pure)......	0	30	30	..
Gulf........................	0	30	30	..
Ashland.....................	0	20	20	..
Signal......................	0	12	12	..
Monsanto...................	49	0	..	49
DuPont.....................	58	30*	..	28*
Dow Badische..............	10	0	..	10

* DuPont may make only 15 million gallons yearly; if so, their purchases would be 43 million gallons yearly.

on a review of published data and partially on the author's estimates.

Phillips is the number one seller of cyclohexane, with sales of approximately 100 million gallons a year and a resultant income in excess of $25 million. Continental Oil is No. 2 with total sales of about 40 million gallons. Altogether there are six companies with sales in excess of 10 million gallons. These six will be joined by AtlanticRichfield and Pontiac, both of whom started up cyclohexane plants in 1965.

Monsanto is the No. 1 purchaser of cyclohexane, with purchases estimated to be 49 million gallons in 1965. DuPont is the largest consumer of cyclohexane, with 1965 consumption being about 58 million gallons; however, as DuPont makes 30 million gallons of cyclohexane, it is the second largest purchaser with purchases of 28 million gallons. Dow Badische is the only other U.S. company buying 10 million gallons or more.

Table 2-8 highlights the importance of the export market to the U.S. companies, as Phillips alone sells more cyclohexane than the three largest U.S. purchasers of cyclohexane. Another interesting point is that DuPont is the only major cyclohexane consumer that makes any of its cyclohexane.

TABLE 2-9—Historical Data—U.S. Production, Number of
Producers and Sales Value of Cyclohexane

| YEAR | No. of Producers | Production Millions of Gallons/Yr. | | | | Average Sales Price ¢/gallon | Total Value of Production Millions of Dollars |
		Total	From Benzene Hydrogenation	From Fractionation of Petroleum Streams	Sales Millions of gallons/yr.		
1953	5	46	28*	18*	18	37	17
1954	5	34	30*	4*	10*	37*	13*
1955	3	37*	30*	7*	10*	36*	13*
1956	4	41	31*	10*	11*	36*	15*
1957	5	71	37*	34*	41*	35*	25*
1958	4	51	37*	14*	21*	35*	18*
1959	4	60	37*	23*	30*	34*	20*
1960	5	87	50*	37*	47*	34*	30*
1961	5	108	68*	40*	68	33	36
1962	5	133	80*	53*	108	29	39
1963	6	166	98*	68*	127	26	43
1964	6	210	140	70	164	25	53
1965*	10	280	175	75	230	26	73
1970*	..	460	385	75	410	25—28	115—130

Source: U.S. Tariff Commission.   * Estimates.

HISTORICAL DATA

Table 2-9 presents data based on U.S. Tariff Commission reports for 1953 through 1964 and on the author's estimates for 1965 and 1970. Also during the 1954 through 1960 period, the author's estimates for average sales price were used because the U.S. Tariff Commission Reports did not contain average sales price for those years.

These data show a gradual increase in U.S. output from 1953 through 1958 and a rapid rise in output in 1959 and after. Cyclohexane produced both from benzene and by fractionation of petroleum streams has increased in volume but future increases are expected to be by the benzene-hydrogenation route—refer to Figure 2-8.

Average sales price has dropped gradually from 37¢/ gallon in 1954 down to a low of 25¢/gallon in 1964. This drop in sales price has paralleled the drop in benzene prices; most of the cost of cyclohexane is accounted for

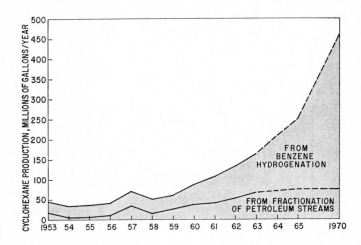

Figure 2-8. U.S. cyclohexane comes from these sources.

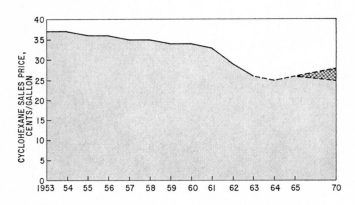

Figure 2-9. Sales price of U.S. cyclohexane follows these trends.

by the cost of the benzene. The price of cyclohexane has recently firmed in line with the increases in benzene price; average sales price in 1965 should approximate 26¢/gallon. Refer to Figure 2-9.

The total value of U.S. production has increased gradually from the neighborhood of $15 million annually in the early 1950s to an estimated $65 million in 1965. It is expected that the value of the U.S. cyclohexane output will pass the $100 million mark in 1968 and be $115 to $130 million by 1970. Refer to Figure 2-10.

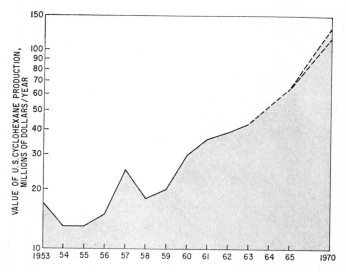

Figure 2-10. Value of U.S. cyclohexane has grown at this rate.

ECONOMICS

The economics of the Phillips operation in which cyclohexane is recovered from petroleum streams is difficult to determine. As Phillips fractionates various constituents from a mixed stream of petroleum, part of the fractionation cost is chargeable to cyclohexane and part to the other hydrocarbon products. Under these conditions Phillips is able to meet any other cyclohexane maker on a price basis.

All other cyclohexane is produced by the hydrogenation of benzene, so the economics of this process will be discussed in detail.

The following case was calculated from data published for the Institut Francais du Petrole process,[8] which is shown in Figure 2-3.

Basis: 20 million gallons of cyclohexane/yr.
U.S. Gulf Coast location
Battery Limits Capital = $660,000 or 3.3¢/gallon of annual capacity
Offsite Capital at 33 percent of B. L. Capital = $220,000
Total Capital = $880,000
or 4.4¢/annual gal.
Direct Operating Costs (minus steam and offgas fuel credits)   = 0.7¢/gallon
Return on Investment = 20 percent before taxes
Sales and Administrative Overhead = 1¢/gallon

The table below shows the required cyclohexane sales price for two cases: one with benzene at 25¢/gallon and one with benzene at 28¢/gallon. These two benzene prices represent the parameters within which benzene should sell in the United States over the next five years unless the U.S. market is upset by benzene made in Puerto Rico, U.S. Foreign-Trade Zones, or Europe. In this table hydrogen is taken at fuel value; also figures are shown for higher hydrogen values.

All figures in ¢/gallon of cyclohexane except the benzene base prices

Benzene price, ¢/gallon of benzene	25	28
Raw material cost (benzene)	20.7	23.2
Hydrogen at fuel value	0.6	0.6
Direct operating costs	0.7	0.7
Subtotal: Out of pocket costs	22.0	24.5

Depreciation at 10% of B. L. Plant	0.3	0.3
Subtotal: Breakeven costs	22.3	24.8
Return on investment at 20% of total capital	0.9	0.9
Subtotal without sales and admin.	23.2	25.7
Sales and admin. overhead	1.0	1.0
Grand total—base case	24.2	26.7
Add to base case for hydrogen obtained by: cryogenic recovery	0.9	0.9
Grand Total	25.1	27.6
or palladium-diffusion recovery	1.4	1.4
Grand Total	25.6	28.1
or made from natural gas	2.0	2.0
Grand Total	26.2	28.7

These data are plotted graphically in Figure 2-11. Also it should be noted that if a company building a hydrogen plant for other purposes, such as hydrocracking, wishes to value the extra hydrogen produced for a cyclohexane plant on an incremental-cost basis, then the hydrogen cost in this case would be the same as that shown for the palladium-diffusion case.

The figures above and in Figure 2-11 show the importance of benzene and hydrogen in determining a satisfactory selling price for cyclohexane; the size of the plant has little effect. As discussed in the section on Manufacture, some refiners can still value hydrogen at fuel value although this situation is changing rapidly because of the advent of hydrocracking. The costs of the hydrogen used in the above table were calculated from published data.[2,3,4,5] These costs were calculated for typical cases; in actual practice, especially for the recovery processes, the costs can very widely. Except for the base case with hydrogen valued at fuel value, the hydrogen costs include a 20 percent return on investment before taxes.

Cyclohexane sells at the same price as the posted price for benzene. Thus a refiner who can charge hydrogen at

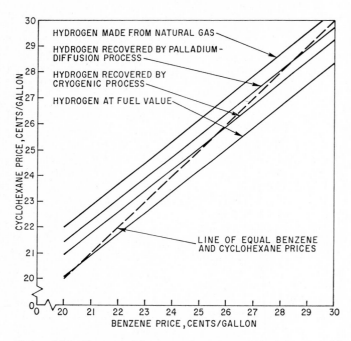

Figure 2-11. These cyclohexane prices are required to earn 20 percent return on investment before taxes in the U.S.

value can earn somewhat more than a 20 percent return on investment before taxes; on the other hand, a manufacturer who must deliberately manufacture hydrogen by reforming natural gas must have a 1.2¢/gallon spread over benzene with benzene valued at 25¢/gallon and a 0.7¢/gallon spread with benzene at 28¢/gallon in order to justify the construction of a cyclohexane unit. Also it is interesting to note that all cyclohexane merchant producers are also benzene producers and can thus adjust their cyclohexane production rates to match their benzene and cyclohexane sales requirements.

THE FUTURE

There are three main areas of uncertainty in the future of cyclohexane. These are: the availability and price of benzene, the export market for cyclohexane, and the value of hydrogen. Each of these is discussed in more detail.

Benzene Price. The price of cyclohexane will continue to be tied to that of benzene as 0.83 gallons of benzene are consumed for each gallon of cyclohexane. However, the future price of benzene is uncertain, primarily because of the effect of a possible buildup in benzene production facilities in Puerto Rico or in Foreign-Trade Zones in the U.S. Benzene in such locations would be produced from low-cost naphtha imported from foreign areas; naphtha is valued less overseas because of a lower demand for gasoline per barrel of crude oil refined. Naphtha ends up in the gasoline pool in a refinery. The decision of the U.S. government will be the determining factor in this possible buildup.[12] If the U.S. benzene market continues to be met by additional facilities for the dealkylation of toluene, then it is expected that the U.S. price for benzene will remain in the 25¢ to 28¢/gallon range for the foreseeable future.

Export Market. The export market accounts for about 45 percent of U.S. cyclohexane production. How much of the present export market can be retained and how much the export market can be expanded in the future will depend on the growth of the foreign markets for nylon and the rapidity with which cyclohexane plants are built abroad. The outcome is not clear at the present time although many experts see a rise in cyclohexane exports, at least in the immediate future.

Hydrogen Value. There is little doubt that the value of hydrogen in the United States will continue to rise over the next five years. Hydrocracking capacity is growing rapidly and this process consumes large quantities of hydrogen and almost always results in the construction of a hydrogen manufacturing unit, since hydrogen from catalytic reformers is not sufficient to meet the hydrocracking requirements. Once a refiner is forced to build a hydrogen plant then logic forces him to view hydrogen as being more valuable than a fuel, although his accounting system may record various costs for hydrogen from the various sources. It is anticipated that over the next few years there will be enough refiners who value catalytic reformer hydrogen at fuel value or can recover hydrogen from waste streams to keep cyclohexane at the same price as that posted for benzene, especially since benzene at times has been known to sell at less than the posted price. However, sometime after 1970 hydrogen should have sufficient value to force a prospective maker of cyclohexane to require a ½ to 1¢/gallon premium over benzene.

Hence, it seems logical to conclude that over the next five years cyclohexane will sell at the same price as benzene; this is expected to be in the 25¢ to 28¢/gallon range.

Literature Cited

1. Stobaugh, Robert B., "Why Do Prices Drop," *Chemical Engineering Progress,* 60: 13-17, December, 1964.
2. Buividas, L. J., H. R., Schmidt, and C. H. Viens. "Integrate Hydrogen Production With Refinery Operations," *Chemical Engineering Progress,* 61: 88-92, May, 1965.
3. McBride, R. B., and D. L. McKinley, "A New Hydrogen Recovery Route," *Chemical Engineering Progress,* 61: 81-85, March, 1965.
4. Stormont, O. H., "Hydrogen Recovery Takes on New Luster," *The Oil and Gas Journal,* 63: 125-128, March 8, 1965.
5. Voogd, J. and Jack Tielrooy, "Make Hydrogen by Naphtha Reforming," *Hydrocarbon Processing & Petroleum Refiner,* 42: 144-148, March, 1963.
6. Sources such as *Hydrocarbon Processing & Petroleum Refiner; Oil, Paint and Drug Reporter; Chemical Engineering; Oil and Gas Journal; Chemical Week;* and *Engineering News*

were used for news items and market and capacity estimates. However, the author takes full responsibility for the final estimates published.

7. *Chemical Engineering Progress*, 61, p. 83, March, 1965.

8. Dufau, F. A., F. Escard, A. C. Haddad, and C. H. Thonon, "High Purity Cyclohexane," *Chemical Engineering Progress*, 60: 43-47, September 1964.

9. Tariff Commission preliminary reports show 1965 production as 280 million gallons; Table 2-9 has been revised accordingly.

10. These companies have added or are adding additional capacity as of Mid-1966.

11. Shipments in 1965 totaled 860 million pounds and production totaled 892 million pounds.

12. See footnote 1, Chapter 5.

3

Styrene

SOME 97 PERCENT of the U.S. styrene monomer is made by the dehydrogenation of ethylbenzene, and about 91 percent of this ethylbenzene is made by the alkylation of benzene with ethylene. Most future styrene capacity will be based on ethylbenzene obtained from alkylation of benzene. Consumption of styrene monomer is expected to grow at the rate of 8 percent a year between 1965 and 1970, thus resulting in a 1970 demand of 4,100[5] million pounds compared with 2,800[5] in 1965.

Polystyrene represents the largest single outlet for styrene monomer and will continue in this role in the future as SBR and export markets decline in importance. A greater percentage of styrene monomer output will be consumed internally in the years ahead as many of the polystyrene makers manufacture their own styrene monomer. Economics indicate that the price for styrene monomer should remain in the 8 to 8½c/pound range from 1965 to 1970; however, as increases in production rate over long periods of time are usually accompanied by decreases in price, the price may drop to 7¢/ pound by 1970. The largest single factor influencing costs is benzene price.

The total value of styrene monomer produced in the U.S. passed the $200 million level in 1963 and will pass approximately $300 million by 1970. Severe price drops in the last few years have kept the total value of styrene production from rising faster, as it increased only 19 percent between 1959 and 1965 compared with a 78 percent increase in production during this period. There are not expected to be many new producers of styrene monomer in the U.S. in the next few years.

MANUFACTURE

All of the styrene monomer produced in the United States is made from ethylbenzene, with the two routes shown below:

Dehydrogenation of ethylbenzene	97 percent
Acetophenone route	3 percent
	100 percent

The ethylbenzene is obtained from the following two main sources:

Alkylation of benzene with ethylene	91 percent
Fractionation from petroleum streams	9 percent
	100 percent

These figures are based on estimates of 1965 production. The two dominant process routes shown above —dehydrogenation of ethylbenzene and alkylation of benzene with ethylene—have always dominated the styrene scene and will continue to do so.

Ethylbenzene is obtained by the alkylation of benzene with either concentrated ethylene or dilute ethylene; these two processes along with fractionation of ethylbenzene from petroleum streams are discussed below as all three of these processes are expected to continue to be commercially important in the future. On the other hand, the manufacture of styrene via the acetophenone route is practiced only by Union Carbide at one of its two styrene plants and it is anticipated that the plant may be shutdown at some future date; hence only the production of styrene by the dehydrogenation of ethylbenzene will be discussed in detail.

Fractionation of Ethylbenzene from Petroleum Streams. This process was introduced commercially by Cosden in 1957; prior to that time all ethylbenzene was made by alkylation of benzene with ethylene. This process is shown in Figure 3-1. Since Cosden's successful commercialization of this process a number of other companies have chosen to use this route; refer to Table 3-1. In Cosden's plant the feedstock to the super fractionating columns is mixed-xylene isomers containing essentially no non-aromatic hydrocarbons boiling in the xylene range. Three 200-foot columns are used in series and operated at high reflux rates; there are over 300 trays in

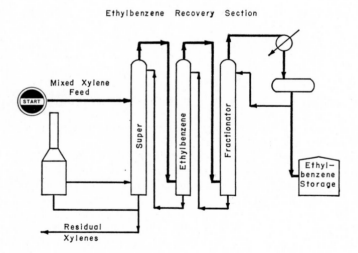

Figure 3-1. Using this equipment arrangement ethylbenzene can be recovered from mixed xylene isomer streams.

TABLE 3-1—U.S. Producers of Ethylbenzene by Fractionation

Company	Location	Ethylbenzene Capacity— Millions of Pounds/Yr.
Allied......................	Frankfort, Pa.	6
Cosden......................	Big Spring, Texas	23
Enjay......................	Baytown, Texas	90
Monsanto...................	Alvin, Texas	40
Sinclair-Koppers............	Houston, Texas	80
Signal......................	Houston, Texas	35
Suntide....................	Corpus Christi, Tex.	30
Tenneco....................	Chalmette, La.	20
Total.................	....	324

series in this operation. Ethylbenzene is separated from its nearest xylene isomer, paraxylene, which boils 3.9° F higher than ethylbenzene. The purity of the ethylbenzene is particularly important because the product styrene purity is determined by the purity of the ethylbenzene.

Ethylbenzene by Alkylation (High-Concentration Ethylene). This process is the traditional one used to make ethylbenzene and accounts for more than 90 percent of the ethylbenzene made by alkylation. This process is shown in Figure 3-2; the chemistry is shown in Figure 3-3. In this process dry benzene and ethylene (95 to 99+ percent purity) are fed into an alkylating tower. Aluminum chloride is ordinarily used as the catalyst, although a phosphoric acid catalyst can also be used. The aluminum chloride combines with the hydrocarbon to form a hydrocarbon-insoluble complex. The reaction products, composed of crude alkylate plus entrained complex, enter the separators where the aluminum chloride complex is separated from the crude mixture. Virtually all of the ethylene fed to the alkylators is reacted; none is recycled and vent losses are negligible. The crude ethylbenzene from the separators is charged to the fractionation system. The high-boiling polyethylbenzenes are separated from the ethylbenzene and sent to the alkylation system

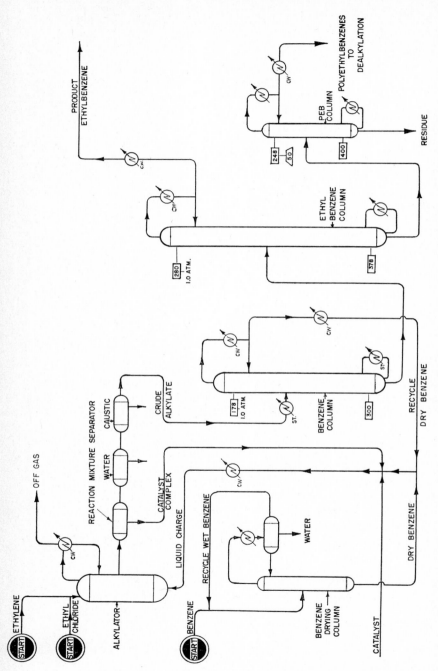

Figure 3-2. Ethylbenzene can be made by alkylating benzene with high concentration ethylene using this process.

for dealkylation. Product ethylbenzene is taken overhead from the ethylbenzene column. Union Carbide is believed to be using an improved version of this process at its plant in Seadrift, Texas. However, details of Carbide's process are not yet available.

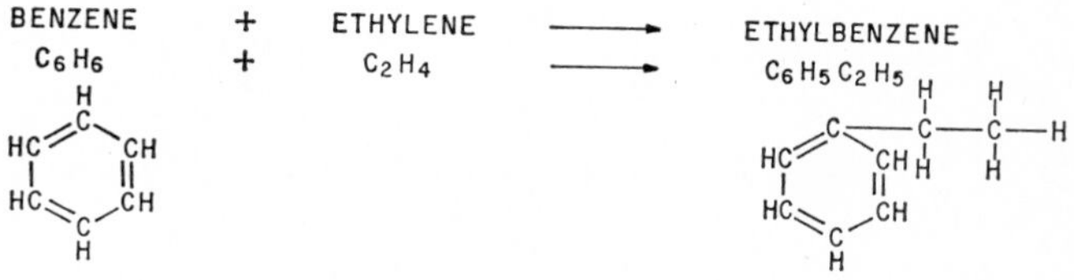

Figure 3-3. Alkylating benzene with ethylene follows this chemistry to give ethylbenzene.

Ethylbenzene by Alkylation (Low-Concentration Ethylene). The special feature of this process is that it can use a feed gas, such as a catalytic cracker off-gas, containing low concentrations of ethylene. Refer to Figure 3-4 for a flowsheet. In this process the ethylene-containing gas and feed benzene are combined with recycle benzene; similarly, recycle polyaromatics are combined with recycle benzene. The combined feeds are raised to reaction temperature and enter the respective reactors. Conversion of the ethylene in the feed gas to ethylbenzene is virtually complete and the polyalkylbenzenes are transalkylated to yield monoalkylated products. The reaction mixture enters the purification system in which light gases are flashed, benzene is separated from ethylbenzene, and ethylbenzene is separated from polyalkybenzenes. There are several plants in the United States that have adopted this process.

Styrene by Dehydrogenation of Ethylbenzene. The flow diagram for this process is shown in Figure 3-5; the

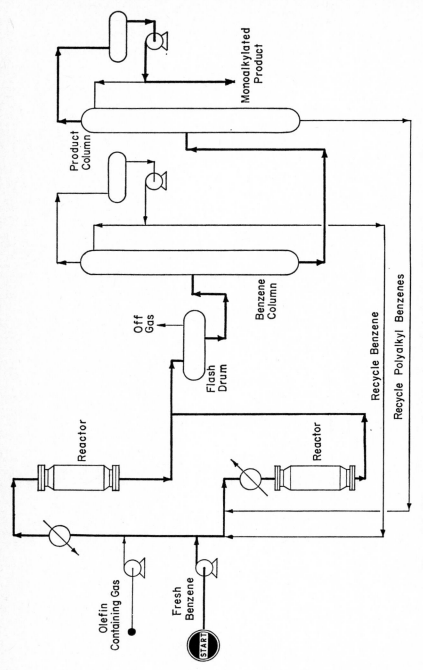

Figure 3-4. This process uses low-concentration ethylene to alkylate benzene for ethylbenzene.

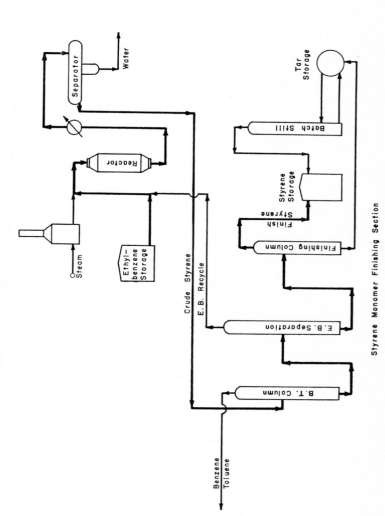

Figure 3-5. Dehydrogenation of ethylbenzene, using this process, results in styrene monomer.

chemistry is shown in Figure 3-6. In this process the fresh ethylbenzene feed is combined with recycle ethylbenzene, mixed with super-heated steam, and charged to the dehydrogenation reactor. The dehydrogenation reaction takes place in the presence of Shell 105 catalyst and at a temperature of 1200-1400° F. A low reaction pressure is used along with a high mole ratio of steam to ethylbenzene.

The effluent from the reactor is condensed and collected in a separator where the steam condensate is withdrawn. Conversion of ethylbenzene to styrene is maintained in the optimum range of 35 to 40 percent per pass by using the reactor pressure and temperature as major control points. The hydrocarbon mixture is separated in the purification section by first removing the benzene and toluene from the styrene and ethylbenzene; these latter two in turn are fractionated in either one column as shown in the flow diagram or in a two-column system. Inhibitors are added and the distillation is carried out at low-temperature, vacuum conditions in order to avoid styrene polymerization. A finally small column is required to separate the finished styrene monomer from the small amounts of polymer and tar formed during the operation.

U.S. Styrene Producers. A list of U.S. styrene makers is shown in Table 3-2. The economics of styrene manufacture are discussed in a separate section.

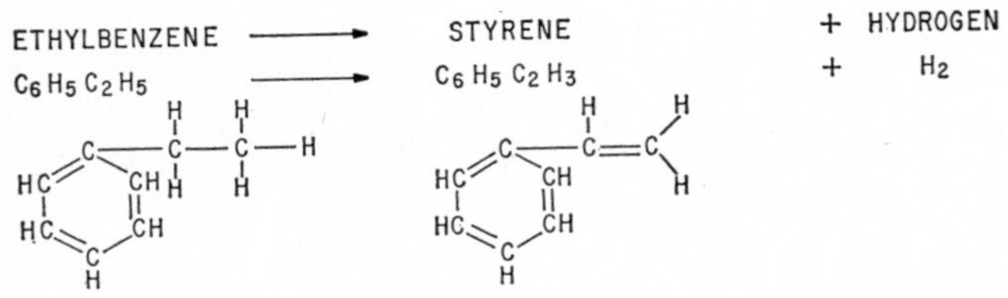

Figure 3-6. Chemistry of dehydrogenation of ethylbenzene to styrene.

TABLE 3-2—U.S. Styrene Monomer Producers

Company	Location	Styrene Capacity— Millions of Pounds/Yr.*
Amoco Chemical	Texas City, Texas	250
Cosden[6]	Big Spring, Texas	100**
Dow	Freeport, Texas	500
Dow	Midland, Mich.	300
El Paso	Odessa, Texas	80
Foster Grant	Baton Rouge, La.	200
Marbon[6]	Baytown, Texas	75***
Monsanto[6]	Texas City, Texas	600**
Shell	Torrance, Calif.	210
Sinclair-Koppers	Houston, Texas	70***
Sinclair-Koppers	Kobuta, Pa.	200
Suntide	Corpus Christi, Texas	60**
Union Carbide	Institute, W. Va.	110****
	Seadrift, Texas	300
Total U.S.		3055

* Unless otherwise noted the ethylbenzene is made by alkylation of benzene with ethylene; styrene monomer is made by dehydrogenation of ethylbenzene. Using this route 0.865 lbs. of benzene and 0.32 lbs. of ethylene are consumed per pound of styrene monomer.
** Some ethylbenzene obtained by fractionating a petroleum stream
*** All ethylbenzene obtained by fractionating a petroleum stream.
**** Ethylbenzene is oxidized to acetophenone, which is hydrogenated to phenylethyl alcohol, which in turn is dehydrated to styrene monomer.

MARKETS

The markets for U.S. styrene monomer are projected to grow about 8 percent a year over the next five years, from an estimated 2,800 million pounds[5] in 1965 to 4,100 million pounds in 1970. This is in spite of the fact that styrene consumption in styrene-butadiene rubber (SBR) is not expected to increase; as discussed below this outlet is expected to account for 20 percent of styrene consumption in 1965 (Table 3-3 and Figure 3-7).

The major consumer of styrene continues to be styrene-type plastic materials, predominantly straight polystyrene or rubber-modified polystyrene. These styrene-type plastic materials accounted for 59 percent of styrene consumption in 1965 and are expected to account for 70 percent by 1970. The markets for styrene-type plastic materials, SBR, and other styrene consumers are discussed in detail below.

TABLE 3-3—Markets for U.S. Styrene Monomer—1965 and 1970

	Millions of Pounds	
	1965	1970
Styrene-type plastic materials		
Straight polystyrene........................	710	1420
Rubber-modified polystyrene...............	640	940
Styrene-butadiene copolymer..............	100	140
All other (includes ABS & SAN)............	190	380
Subtotals: Plastic materials...............	1640	2880
Styrene-butadiene rubber (SBR).............	560	560
Export....................................	350	200
Polyesters................................	140	280
Miscellaneous.............................	110	180
Grand Totals...........................	2800[5]	4100[5]

Styrene-Type Plastic Materials. These materials rank third, behind polyethylene and polyvinyl chloride, in the over-all plastics race. Their importance to styrene monomer producers continues to grow; as recently as 1960, they consumed only 50 percent of styrene output. Molding at 52 percent of total styrene plastics and extrusion at 16 percent represent the largest two uses of the styrene-type plastics (Table 3-4 and Figure 3-8). The four main types of styrene-type plastic materials are: (1) straight polystyrene, (2) rubber-modified polystyrene, (3) styrene-butadiene copolymer, and (4) others, including acrylonitrile-butadiene-styrene (ABS) and styrene-acrylonitrile (SAN). Each of these will be discussed in detail below.

Straight polystyrene. Manufacture of this material will consume 710 million pounds of styrene monomer in 1965, or 25 percent of over-all styrene monomer output and 43 percent of all styrene monomer used in plastic materials. Straight polystyrene, often called general-purpose polystyrene, is widely used in molding and extrusion applicatons to make such items as toys, appliances, household wares, and packaging items. Its low price of around 15c/pound makes it a bargain plastic and when calcu-

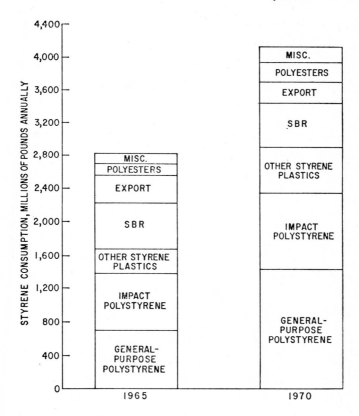

Figure 3-7. U.S. markets for styrene follow this pattern.

lated on a price/cubic inch basis it is the lowest cost of all plastics. However, it has one main disadvantage—it has insufficient resistance to impact and it has a tendency to form jagged edges when it is fractured. These faults are greatly reduced by incorporating rubber into

TABLE 3-4—Estimated U.S. Markets for Styrene-Type Plastic Materials—1965

	Millions of Pounds	% of Total
Molding..	970	52
Extrusion......................................	300	16
Textile and paper treating and coating.......	140	8
Export...	120	6
Emulsion paint...............................	40	2
All other uses (including foam and foamable materials).......................	290	16
Total....................................	1860	100

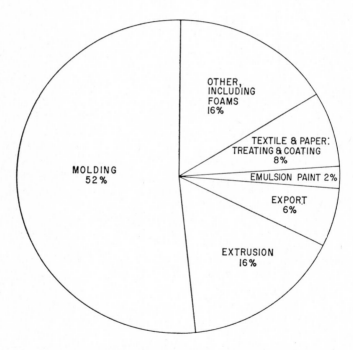

Figure 3-8. Uses of styrene-type plastics showed this pattern in the U.S. in 1965.

the polymer; the resultant rubber-modified polystyrene is discussed below. However, before this discussion it is desirable to review the combined markets of the straight and rubber-modified polystyrenes:

	Percent
Packaging	22
Toys, luggage, sports goods, premiums	13
Housewares	11
Radio, TV, lighting, and signs	8
Refrigeration	7
Appliances	3
Miscellaneous	36
	100%

A 15 percent growth rate is projected for the next five years; thus this material will consume 35 percent of total styrene monomer output in 1970.

Polystyrene is made by one of the following four techniques: (1) Suspension polymerization, which is carried out with a suspension of small styrene globules in water in agitated kettles on a batch basis; as the reaction progresses, the styrene droplets harden into polymer beads in the 40-60 mesh size range; (2) Mass polymerization, which is carried out in either a batch or continuous process and results in high-purity product, as only a reaction initiator or catalyst is used in addition to the styrene; (3) Emulsion polymerization, which is used more in the production of latexes and SBR than in the production of straight polystyrene; and (4) Solution polymerization, which effects the reaction in a solvent in which the monomer, and sometimes the polymer, is soluble. These techniques were listed in order of descending commercial importance.

Rubber-modified polystyrene. Manufacture of this material will consume 640 million pounds of styrene monomer in 1965, or 23 percent of over-all styrene monomer output and 39 percent of all styrene monomer used in plastic materials. As mentioned above, this material was developed to make polystyrene more resistant to impact—hence, it is frequently called "impact polystyrene." It lacks the transparency of the general-purpose polystyrene and so its coloring possibilities are limited to opaque products. The consumption of this material is not expected to grow as much as that of general-purpose polystyrene because of the severe inroads being made in its markets by ABS plastics, especially in the appliance, refrigeration, and luggage fields. Consumption of styrene in this market is expected to grow only 8 percent annually over the next five years, and thus it will continue to consume about 23 percent of styrene monomer output.

These high-impact polymers are made either by mechanical blending of polystyrene or by graft polymerization of styrene on SBR rubber. In the latter method, styrene monomer is polymerized by one of the four methods discussed above, but in the presence tiny particles of SBR rubber suspended in the reactor.

Styrene-butadiene copolymer, ABS, SAN, and other. These uses of styrene monomer are relatively small; they are expected to account for consumption of 290 million pounds of styrene monomer in 1965, or only about 10 percent of all monomer used and 18 percent of all styrene monomer used in plastic materials. Styrene-butadiene copolymers contain predominantly styrene; they are used, mainly in latex form, in surface coatings and in the finishing operations of the textile and paper industries. ABS is widely used in appliances, automotive, luggage, telephones, shoe heels, and plastic pipe; it is one of the fastest growing plastics, with an annual growth rate of 20 percent. This material is made a variety of ways and contains varying amounts of styrene depending on the desired properties of the final product. SAN resins offer good chemical resistance with good moldability and unlimited coloring possibilities. They usually contain 70 to 75 percent styrene and are made by using mass polymerization techniques.

The consumption of styrene in these materials is expected to grow slightly more than 12 percent a year, so by 1970 they will account for 13 percent of total styrene monomer consumption.

A detailed listing of all companies making styrene-type plastic materials is shown in Table 3-5. Detailed information on all plant capacities is not available; however, several points stand out. Firstly, there are only four companies that make all five types of materials—Goodrich, Dow, Monsanto, and Sinclair-Koppers. Secondly, there are a large number of companies—some 41 in all—that make at least one type of styrene plastic material.

The five largest producers of polystyrene are: Dow, Monsanto, Foster Grant, Sinclair-Koppers, and Union Carbide. Each of these has an annual capacity greater than 100 million pounds, with Dow and Monsanto being considerably larger than this.

Styrene-Butadiene Rubber. SBR has long been one of the mainstays of the styrene monomer business, especially since virtually all of the SBR manufacturers purchase their styrene. In 1960 SBR consumed 31 percent of the U.S. output of styrene monomer, but this percentage has gradually been dropping. In 1965 production of SBR will approximate 1,300,000 long tons, including the carbon black and oil which are added to the styrene-butadiene polymer. The styrene consumed in this SBR will be 560 million pounds, or 20 percent of total U.S. styrene output. SBR's main outlet is in tires, where it is used to make the tire treads and carcasses. In recent years there have been a number of new rubbers introduced with the idea of capturing part of the tire market. Specifically, these are butyl, *cis*-polyisoprene, *cis*-polybutadiene, and ethylene/propylene terpolymers.

Cis-polybutadiene has had some success in the tire mar-

TABLE 3-5—U.S. Producers of Styrene-Type Plastics Materials

	Molding	Textile and Paper Treating and Coating	Emulsion Paint	Extrusion	All Other Uses
Amoco Chemical..........					X
Beacon Chem. Ind..........					X
J.T. Baker Chem..........	X			X	
Borden....................		X	X		X
Brand Plastics.............	X				
Charles S. Tanner Co.......	X				
Cosden...................				X	
Dow.....................	X	X	X	X	X
DeSoto Chem. Coatings....					X
DuPont...................					X
Fiberfil...................	X				
Foster Grant..............	X				
Firestone.................		X	X		X
General Tire & Rubber.....		X	X		
Goodrich..................	X	X	X	X	X
Goodyear.................	X	X	X		X
Gordon Chemical..........	X				
W. R. Grace..............	X			X	X
International Latex........		X			
Pfaulder Permutit.........					X
Monsanto.................	X	X	X	X	X
Massachusetts Plastic......	X				
Morton Chem..............		X			
Onyx Chemicals...........					X
Penn. Ind. Chem..........					X
Polymer Corp.............					X
Polyvinyl Chemicals.......					X
Rexall....................	X			X	
Richardson Co.............	X				
Rinshed-Mason............			X		
Rohm & Haas.............					X
Shell.....................	X				X
Sinclair-Koppers..........	X	X	X	X	X
Solar Chem...............	X				
Ticonderoga Chem.........	X				
Union Carbide.............	X			X	X
U.S. Rubber..............	X	X	X	X	
United Cork..............					X
Staley Manufacturing......					X
Washburn-Purex..........		X			X
Wica Chemicals...........		X			

Includes manufacturers producing: Straight polystyrene, Rubber modified polystyrene, Styrene-butadiene copolymers, and all other types, including acrylonitrile-butadiene-styrene plastics (ABS) and styrene-acrylonitrile copolymer (SAN).
Basic reference Source: U.S. Tariff Commission.

ket but most recently there has been considerable attention focused on ethylene/propylene terpolymers (EPT). This terpolymer is predominantly ethylene and propylene and thus enjoys low-cost raw materials; additionally, it has outstanding ozone and weather resistance, high heat resistance, chemical resistance, and a lower modulus than SBR. The EPT tread will wear at about the same rate, or possibly slightly lower, than SBR. Its cost is presently higher than SBR but it can be oil extended and it is expected that costs will drop once larger-scale production starts. EPT has at least three major hurdles to overcome before it will be used in large volumes in tires: (1) It is not compatible with any highly unsaturated polymers unless the non-routine peroxide curing systems are used; thus extremely clean conditions must be maintained for the rubber production lines; (2) It has poor adhesion qualities so that extensive modifications to existing tire-building machines would be necessary before EPT could be used; and (3) Extensive testing is needed to prove that a rubber is satisfactory for tire use. Hence it appears that it will be some time before EPT makes serious inroads into SBR's tire markets, although the increased competition from this and other rubbers is expected to prevent SBR from recording any growth over the next five years. The importance of tires is illustrated by the fact that tires and tire products use over 65 percent of the general purpose elastomers consumed in the United States.

Therefore, in 1970 it is expected that styrene consumption in SBR will continue to approximate 560 million pounds, which will equal 14 percent of styrene output in that year.

An emulsion polymerization process is used to make SBR from styrene and butadiene; in this process emulsifying agents are used to keep the organic phase well dispersed through the aqueous medium. A chain-terminating agent is used to obtain the correct chain length.

A list of SBR manufacturers is shown in Table 3-6.

TABLE 3-6—U.S. Producers of SBR Rubber

| Company | Location | Capacity—Long tons/yr. | | Estimated styrene consumption in 1965— millions of pounds /year** |
		Weight of polymer, oil, and black	Weight of polymer only*	
American Synthetic	Louisville, Ky.	110,000	68,000	38
Copolymer Rubber	Baton Rouge, La.	130,000	81,000	45
Firestone Tire	Akron, Ohio	50,000	31,000	17
	Lake Charles, La.	220,000	136,000	76
Genera l Tire	Odessa, Texas	70,000	43,000	24
Goodrich-Gulf	Institute, W. Va.	100,000	62,000	35
	Port Neches, Tex.	160,000	99,000	55
Goodyear Tire	Akron, Ohio	30,000	19,000	10
	Houston, Texas	270,000	167,000	93
Phillips	Borger, Texas	110,000	68,000	38
Shell	Torrance, Calif.	100,000	62,000	35
Texas-U.S. Chem.	Port Neches, Tex.	160,000	99,000	55
United Carbon	Baytown, Tex.	80,000	50,000	28
Other		30,000	19,000	10
Total		1,620,000	1,004,000	560

* Composition of SBR assumed to be: polymer 62%, black 23%, and oil 16%.
** Calculated on assumption that polymer is 23.5% styrene.

Other Markets consume 21 percent of the U.S. styrene monomer output; this is split as follows: export 13 percent, polyesters 5 percent, and miscellaneous 3 percent. Polyesters market growth is expected to be substantial between now and 1970; on the other hand, there is expected to be some decrease in styrene monomer exports as the European capacity builds up. Thus by 1970 this total category will consume only 16 percent of the U.S. styrene, with the breakdown being as follows: export 5 percent, polyesters 7 percent, and miscellaneous 4 percent.

INDIVIDUAL COMPANIES

Dow historically has been the largest producer of styrene monomer, and it continues to hold that title with a capacity of 800 million pounds, or 26 percent of U.S. capacity. Dow's production is split between Midland, Michigan and Freeport, Texas; hence Monsanto's Texas City plant, with a capacity of 600 million pounds annually, is the largest styrene monomer plant in the world. It accounts for 20 percent of U.S. capacity. Dow has indicated that it intends to continue its leadership in the world styrene business, as it has recently announced its first styrene monomer plant in Europe.

Dow and Monsanto traditionally have been the two largest merchant sellers of styrene as most of the other styrene monomer makers, being considerably smaller than Dow and Monsanto, had smaller quantities of styrene available for the open market. However, recently Amoco and Union Carbide have started up plants of 250 and 300 million pounds per year, respectively; and it is believed that these two are large-scale merchant sellers. Thus as indicated in Table 3-7, there are believed to be five companies selling between 150 and 250 million pounds annually: Dow, Monsanto, Amoco, Union Carbide, and Shell.

TABLE 3-7—Major Sellers and Buyers of Styrene Monomer
(United States — 1965 estimates)

Exact quantities of styrene sales cannot be calculated but it is believed that each of the following companies will sell between 150 and 250 million pounds a year, including export sales. No other company is believed to to be selling as much as 100 million pounds a year.

Amoco Chemicals	Shell
Dow	Union Carbide
Monsanto	

In 1965 there will be a total of about 1,250 million pounds sold versus 2,800 total consumption and export[5]; of this total amount sold, the export markets and SBR markets will account for 73 percent of the total. Thus the major styrene monomer purchasers in the United States are SBR manufacturers. Following are estimated purchases for 1965 of those companies buying 40 million pounds or more:

Company	Purchases—Million of Pounds/Year
Goodyear	103
Firestone	93
Goodrich-Gulf	90
Texas-U.S. Chemicals	55
Copolymer Rubber	45

Many of the polystyrene makers are either small-volume consumers or make their own styrene monomer. Thus the large-scale purchasers of styrene monomer are the SBR companies. Shell is the only SBR maker that makes its own styrene.

Among the purchasers in the U.S., Goodyear is first with 103 million pounds, Firestone second at 93 million pounds, and Goodrich-Gulf third at 90 million pounds; Texas-U.S. Chemical and Copolymer Rubber are the only other companies purchasing over 40 million pounds a year.

Because of the large number of sellers and buyers, and because styrene can be transported easily, no one company can dominate the styrene market.

HISTORICAL DATA

Table 3-8 presents data based on U.S. Tariff Commission reports for 1953 through 1964 and on the author's estimates for 1965 and 1970.

TABLE 3-8—Historical Data: U.S. Production, Number of Producers and Sales Value of Styrene Monomer

Year	Production millions of pounds/yr.	Sales millions of pounds/yr.	Number of producers	Average sales value, ¢/pound, for all styrene sold	Value of total styrene production, millions of dollars/yr.
1953.....	798	470	5	16	128
1954.....	703	329	5	16	112
1955.....	1014	454	5	17	172
1956.....	1176	574	6	16	188
1957.....	1166	625	7	13	152
1958.....	1224	683	8	12	147
1959.....	1571	916	8	12	189
1960.....	1745	1042	8	11	192
1961.....	1762	996	8	11	194
1962.....	1942	1018	10	10	194
1963.....	2154	1096	12	9.3	200
1964.....	2571	1368	12	8.1	208
1965**...	2875	1500	11*	8.0	230
1970**...	4200	1900	..	7.0—8.5	290—360

* Number of producers reduced by one when Sinclair-Koppers partnership took over Koppers plant at Kobuta, Pa.
** Estimates.
Source: U.S. Tariff Commission.

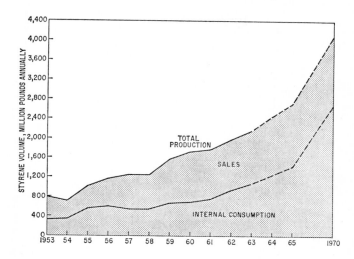

Figure 3-9. Production, sales and internal consumption of U.S. styrene, 1953-1970.

These data show a steady increase in U.S. total styrene monomer production and a corresponding decline in styrene price. Refer to Figures 3-9 and 3-10, respectively. As volume has approximately trebled from the 1953-55 period to a total volume of 2,800 million pounds in 1965, the styrene price has dropped by 50 percent to a level of 8¢/pound in 1965.

Thus there has been a steady, though not spectacular, increase in total value of styrene produced; in 1965 this value will hit $224 million (refer to Figure 3-11). This was only 19 percent over the 1959 total of $180 million while total production during this time increased 78 percent, from 1,571 million pounds annually to 2,800 million pounds annually.

There are two other points of interest: (1) Approxi-

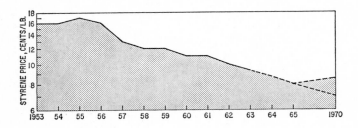

Fig. 3-10. U.S. sales price of styrene has shown this pattern, 1953-1970.

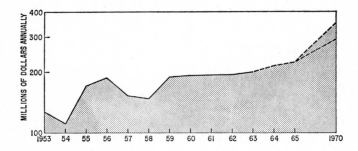

Figure 3-11. Notice the steadily increasing value of U.S. styrene production, 1953-1970.

mately half of the total styrene produced is used internally; and (2) the number of producers has gradually increased through the years so that there are presently 11 in the U.S.—up from five only 10 years ago. This increase in the number of producers has also helped to put pressure on styrene price.

ECONOMICS

As indicated in the section on manufacturing, virtually all of the styrene in the United States is made by the dehydrogenation of ethylbenzene; and some 91 percent of the ethylbenzene is made by alkylation of benzene with ethylene and 9 percent is obtained by fractionation from petroleum streams. Although production of ethylbenzene by alkylation is the dominate route, it is still worthwhile to explore the economics of obtaining ethylbenzene by the fractionation route as several of the styrene plants constructed in recent years obtained either part or all of their ethylbenzene via this route. Each route will be discussed in turn.

Styrene from Ethylbenzene Obtained by Alkylation.

The latest two styrene monomer plants built in the U.S. were built by Badger Co. for Union Carbide and Amoco Chemical. Details of the investment and operating costs have not been published although the plants are reported to use a Union Carbide high-yield alkylation process and an improved direct hydrogenation process, based on Cosden know-how. The Union Carbide plant, with a capacity of 300 million pounds annually, is the largest single integrated styrene plant ever built. It has been speculated that Carbide's process involves molecular sieve catalysis in the alkylation step and Linde's sieve trays; however, details have not been published.

It is generally felt that each of these two plants represent a comparatively low-cost operation, and probably lower in cost than those in the case that follows. The following analysis was calculated on the yields presented in Table 3-2, published data,[1] and on the use of the 0.6 factor for ratioing investment costs. Although the results are approximate, the fact that benzene and ethylene costs represent roughly 70 percent of total operating costs insures some degree of accuracy.

Basis: 200 million pounds of styrene monomer/year.
       U. S. Gulf Coast location.

Battery Limits Capital	= $10	million or 5¢/ annual pound of styrene
Offsite Capital at 33% of B. L.	= $ 3.3 million	
Total Capital	⟳$13.3	million or 6.7¢/ annual pound of styrene

Direct Operating costs	= 1.5¢/pound
Return on Investment	= 20% before taxes
Sales and Admin. Overhead	= 0.5¢/pound

The table below shows the effect benzene value has on required styrene sales prices.

	All figures in ¢/pound of styrene except the benzene base prices	
Benzene price, ¢/gallon	25	28
Raw material cost—benzene	3.0	3.3
—ethylene, at 4¢/pound	1.3	1.3
Direct operating costs	1.5	1.5
Subtotal: Out of pocket costs	5.8	6.1
Depreciation, at 10% of B. L. Plant	0.5	0.5
Subtotal: Breakeven costs	6.3	6.6
Return on Investment, at 20%	1.3	1.3
Subtotal without sales & admin.	7.6	7.9
Sales & admin. overhead	0.5	0.5
Grand Total	8.1	8.4

The grand total represents the sales value required to justify a new plant; the out-of-pocket costs represent the sales value required to keep from shutting down an existing plant.

These figures are for a plant with a capacity of 200 million pounds a year operating at capacity. Although Union Carbide and Amoco both have plants with a larger capacity, it is not reasonable to assume that a plant will be operating at full capacity during the payout period; thus while these new plants incorporate substantial improvements over conventional practice, it is doubtful that they could earn a satisfactory profit at much below 8¢/pound as long as raw material prices stay in their present ranges. Figure 3-12 shows the effect of change in benzene price on required styrene price.

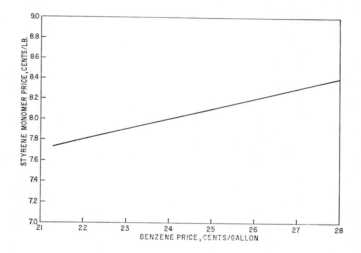

Figure 3-12. Styrene price required to earn 20 percent return on investment before taxes based on benzene alkylation.

Styrene from Ethylbenzene Obtained by Fractionation.

The original plant using this route was Cosden's 20 million pound a year plant built in 1957 and since expanded. The most recent was Marbon's 75 million a year plant which went onstream in 1963; ethylbenzene is obtained from the adjacent facility of Enjay Chemical. As the economics of this operation are very sensitive to capital costs, the economics will be examined on the basis of 20 and 75 million pound/year capacities.[2]

Basis: U.S. Gulf Coast location.
Value of mixed xylene feed containing ethylbenzene =
value of xylenes after ethylbenzene removed = 17¢/gal-
lon = 2.34¢/pound. Xylene feed contains 28 percent
ethylbenzene. Sales and admin. overhead = 0.5¢/pound

I. 20 million pound/year styrene capacity
Battery limits capital = $3 million or 15¢/annual pound of
styrene
Offsite capital at 33% of B. L. = $1 million

Total capital   = $4 million or
                         20¢/annual pound of
                         styrene

Direct operating costs = 2.2¢/pound of styrene

II. 75 million pound/year styrene capacity
Battery limits capital = $6.6 million or 9¢/annual pound
of styrene
Offsite capital at 33% of B. L. = $2.2 million

Total capital   = $8.8 million or
                         12¢/annual pound
                         of styrene

Direct operating costs = 1.8¢/pound of styrene

	All figures in ¢/pound of styrene except the capacity bases	
Plant capacity, millions of pounds of styrene annually	20	75
Value of ethylbenzene in xylene stream:		
Raw material (1.14 x 2.34)	2.7	2.7
Product credit (0.07 x 2¢/lb.)	−0.1	−0.1
Net raw material cost	2.6	2.6
Direct operating costs	2.2	1.8
Subtotal: Out of pocket costs	4.8	4.4
Depreciation at 10% of B. L. plant	1.5	0.9
Subtotal: Break-even costs	6.3	5.3
Return on investment at 20%	4.0	2.4
Subtotal without sales & admin.	10.3	7.7
Sales & admin. overhead	0.5	0.5
Grand Total	10.8	8.2

The grand total represents the sales value required to
justify a new plant; the out-of-pocket costs represent the
sales value required to keep from shutting down an exist-

ing plant. These figures indicate that once a plant of this nature has been built its operating costs will be so low that it can continue to operate in the face of depressed styrene prices; also the figures reveal the relatively small importance of raw material value, that is as long as the xylenes (without ethylbenzene) leaving the unit are valued the same as the xylene feed (with ethylbenzene).

Capital plays a very important part in determining a required sales value of styrene to justify a new plant; the differential in required sales value for a 20 million pound/year plant and one of 75 million pounds/year is striking. Refer to Figure 3-13.

A possible factor which can change the economic picture is the upgrading of the remaining ortho, para, and

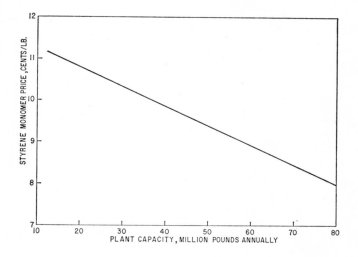

Figure 3-13. Styrene price required to earn 20 percent return on investment before taxes based on ethylbenzene fractionation.

meta xylene isomers; Cosden uses part of its ethylbenzene recovery equipment to separate the orthoxylene.

THE FUTURE

The future of styrene monomer clearly is tied to the future of the polystyrene plastics. Styrene monomer has some degree of protection because some of the newer plastics, such as ABS, which are expected to supplant impact polystyrene in some of the markets still contain some styrene.

SBR will continue to decline in importance as other styrene monomer markets grow while SBR remains constant.

The outlook for the export market is somewhat uncertain; however, compared with total U.S. production it is not too significant. Its relative degree of importance is due primarily to the fact that about 50 percent of styrene is sold on the open market; thus exports account for 25 to 30 percent of total sales, compared with only 13 percent of total production.

The styrene business is becoming more of an integrated business in which the styrene monomer is consumed internally by a polystyrene maker; the amount of styrene monomer consumed internally is projected to grow from 52 percent in 1965 to 66 percent in 1970.

As the external sales markets will consume a smaller proportion of styrene it will become increasingly difficult for a newcomer to enter the styrene monomer business. Part of this picture is that the rubber companies, who are still the largest purchasers of styrene monomer, were once thought to be planning to enter the styrene manufacturing business on a widespread basis—in 1956 Firestone announced that it would build a plant but did not do so presumably because of a drop in styrene price from 16c down to 12c a pound, and other rubber companies were rumored to be considering plans. Now with styrene priced at 8c/pound and with SBR consumption expected to remain constant, the rubber companies are not expected to enter the styrene manufacturing business.

The section on Economics revealed that a very large capacity styrene plant is required to justify construction based on ethylbenzene obtained by fractionation; at today's prices, a plant of about 80 million pounds a year is required. Since there are a limited number of petroleum streams of adequate size containing a high concentration of ethylbenzene, it appears that most of the new plant capacity added will be based on ethylbenzene obtained from alkylation of benzene with ethylene. Using the route, assuming a plant of 200 million pounds or larger and a benzene price of 25 to 28c/gallon, it appears that a styrene price of 8.0 to 8.5c/pound is required to justify construction of a new styrene plant; even if benzene should become available at a few cents under 25c/gallon, styrene monomer would not be expected to sell at any significant level below 8c/pound.

Thus it seems reasonable to conclude that styrene prices will remain in the 8.0 to 8.5c/pound range for the foreseeable future. However, a recent study by the author showed that substantial increases in production rate are generally accompanied by substantially lower prices;[3] based on these studies a drop in the price of styrene monomer to 7¢/pound by 1970 seems reasonable.

With 1970 production estimated to be 4,100 million pounds,[5] and with the price between 7¢ and 8.5¢/pound, the value of styrene produced in the United States in 1970 is expected to be $290 to $350 million. Refer to Figure 3-11.

Literature Cited

1. Sherwood, Peter W. and R. G. Edmonds, "Starting a Petrochemical Industry," *Hydrocarbon Processing & Petroleum Refiner*, 44: 119-125, January, 1965.

2. Calculated by the author based on data presented in: Jenkins, Jerry G., "How Cosden Makes Polystyrene from Crude Oil," *The Oil and Gas Journal,* 63: 78-86, January 18, 1965.

3. See reference 1, Chapter 2.

4. See Reference 3, Chapter 1 for literature references.

5. Tariff Commission preliminary reports show 1965 production as 2.875 billion pounds. Table 3-8 has been revised for 1965 and 1970.

6. These companies have added or are adding additional capacity as of mid-1966.

4

Phenol

SOME 96 PERCENT of U.S. phenol is made synthetically, and about 43 percent of this synthetic phenol is made by the cumene route. Most future additions to U.S. capacity will be by this route so that by 1970, 52 percent of synthetic phenol will be cumene-based; the amount of phenol from natural sources will continue to be relatively small.

Consumption of phenol is expected to grow at the rate of 5 percent a year over the next five years, thus resulting in a 1970 demand of 1,500[5] million pounds compared with 1,180[5] in 1965. Phenolic resins account for about 50 percent of U.S. phenol consumption and will probably account for 54 percent by 1970. No other outlet consumes as much as 10 percent of U.S. output and this will still be the case in 1970.

The largest single item affecting phenol manufacturing costs is benzene price; additionally, the value of propylene to a refiner and sales value of the byproduct acetone are important to the profitability of cumene-based plants.

Rather severe price drops have resulted in the value of phenol output being about the same in 1965 as in 1960, although production increased by 50 percent during this period. In 1970 phenol output should be $133 to $142 million versus $112 million in 1965. The price of phenol is not expected to rise from the 1965 level and could drop by as much as ½¢/pound depending on supply/demand situations that exist over the next few years. A new producer of phenol has the difficult problem of establishing a distribution system to sell to the many phenol outlets; thus some of the new plants will be based on cumene manufactured by refiners and sold to chemical companies who will then convert the cumene to phenol.

MANUFACTURE

Phenol is obtained from two main sources:

Natural sources	4%
Synthetic sources	96%
	100%

Synthetic phenol is obtained by the following main process routes:

Cumene	43%
Raschig	19%
Chlorobenzene (Chlorination)	18%
Sulfonation	16%
Other	4%
	100%

Natural sources of phenol have gradually declined in importance; in 1953 they accounted for 7 percent of U.S. phenol production. They will not be discussed further.

The cumene route to phenol was introduced in 1955 and has captured a larger share of phenol production each year while the other process routes have been losing their relative share of phenol production. Each of these routes will be discussed in detail.

Cumene. This route has two distinct processes: (1) Cumene is made by alkylating benzene with propylene and (2) phenol and acetone are made by oxidizing cumene and cleaving the hydroperoxide from the resulting molecule. The chemistry for these two processes is shown in Figure 4-1.

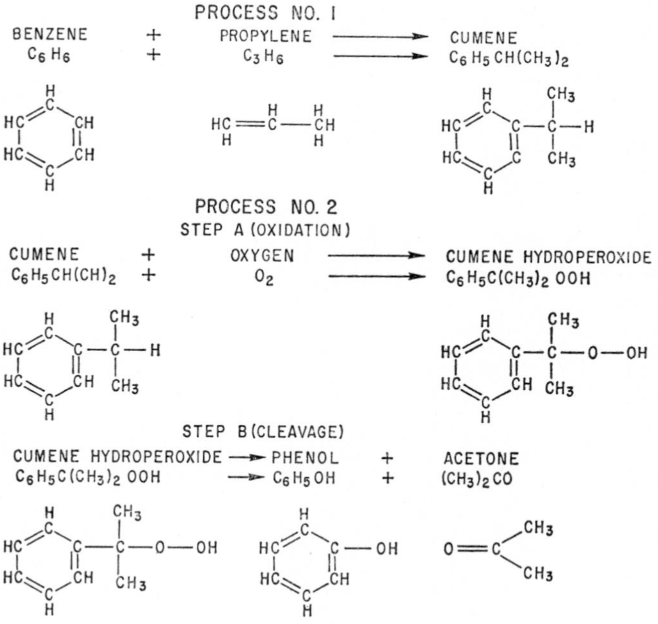

Figure 4-1. Chemistry of the phenol from cumene process.

The flow sheet for the manufacture of cumene is shown in Figure 4-2. In this process benzene is mixed with propylene in a combined feed surge drum and the resulting charge is fed to the reactor. A solid phosphoric acid catalyst is used; it is maintained in separate beds in the reactor. As the reaction is exothermic, suitable propane quench is provided between beds for temperature control purposes.

The reactor effluent goes to the depropanizer; the depropanizer bottoms stream passes to the benzene recovery column, where unreacted benzene goes overhead. The crude cumene product from the bottom of the benzene column is purified in a rerun column to produce specification cumene (over 99.8 percent).

The flow sheet for the manufacture of phenol and acetone is shown in Figure 4-3. In this process oxidation is carried out in special contactors designed for intimate mixing of gas and liquid. The reaction is carried out at 260° F at a pressure slightly above atmospheric. The effluent from the oxidizer passes through a condenser for recovery of cumene and other organics and is then charged to the cleavage vessel. Cumene hydroperoxide is produced in the oxidizer; this is decomposed to phenol and acetone in the cleavage vessel. This cleavage is caused by contact with dilute sulfuric acid (10-25 percent) in an agitated vessel at 130-150° F. The conversion of cumene is very low as the effluent from the water wash tower is 76 percent cumene and only 14 percent phenol and 8 percent acetone.

This mixture is then separated in a series of conventional distillation columns. Acetone goes overhead from the first column, cumene from the second, and alpha-methylstyrene from the third. Product phenol goes overhead from the fourth column and is further purified by crystallization. Acetophenone, containing small amounts of tar and phenol, is taken from the bottom of the column and may require further purification for sales.

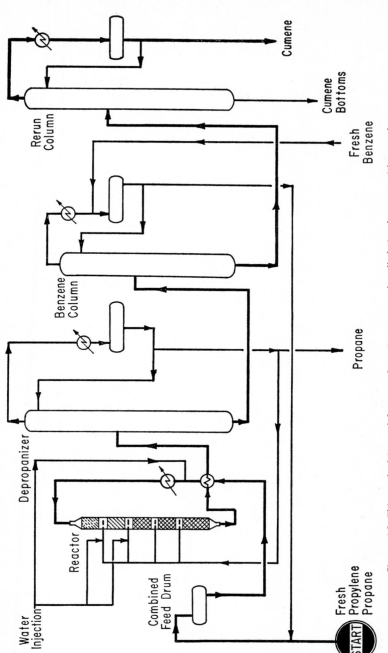

Figure 4-2. This method is used for manufacturing cumene by alkylating benzene with propylene.

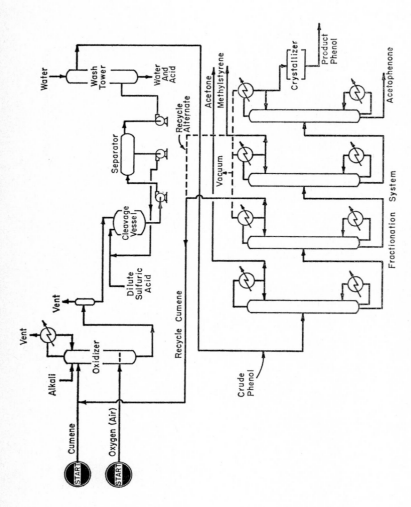

Figure 4-3. Phenol is made from cumene using this arrangement.

This cumene process is ordinarily the only one of the major routes used which is thought of as being a "petrochemical process." The other processes depend economically to a large extent on the availability of low-cost HCl; chlorine and caustic soda; or sulfuric acid and caustic soda. These remaining routes are described very briefly; details on these have been published.[1]

Raschig (Regenerative) Process. This route has two distinct processes: (1) Benzene is chlorinated to chlorobenzene with an HCl-air mixture; a catalyst of chlorides of copper and iron is used. Conversion is 10 to 15 percent per pass. (2) Chlorobenzene is hydrolyzed with steam to produce phenol and HCl. The HCl is recycled for use in the first process. The conversion in this step is also 10 to 15 percent.

The chemistry of these two reactions is shown in Figure 4-4; the flow sheet is shown in Figure 4-5. Vari-

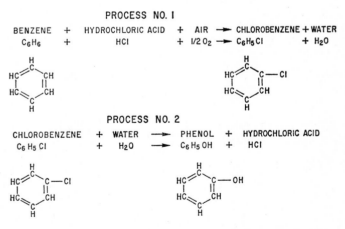

Figure 4-4. Chemistry of phenol via the Raschig process.

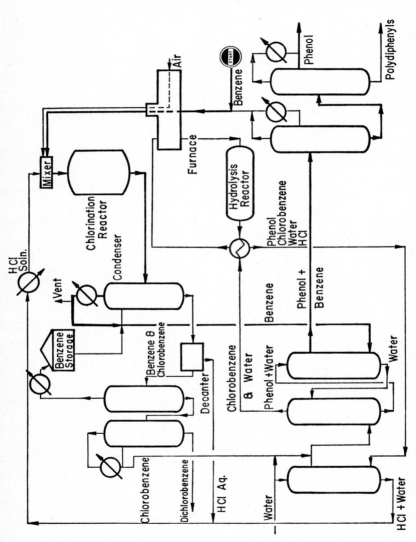

Figure 4-5. Using this arrangement phenol can be made from chlorobenzene via benzene and hydrogen chloride using the Raschig process.

ous modifications have been made in the original Raschig process which give better yields and better utilization of equipment. High temperatures are used and special materials are required to reduce corrosion.

Chlorobenzene (Chlorination) Process. This route has three distinct steps: (1) Benzene and chlorine are reacted to give monochlorobenzene, HCl, and about 5 percent polychlorobenzenes. (2) Monochlorobenzene is hydrolyzed with caustic soda to give sodium phenate. (3) Sodium phenate is mixed with HCl, from the first step, to form phenol and sodium chloride. The sodium chloride

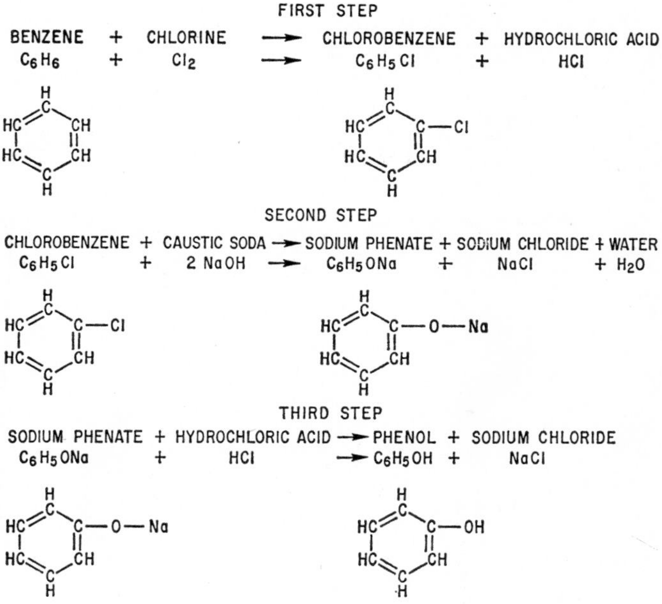

FIRST STEP

BENZENE + CHLORINE → CHLOROBENZENE + HYDROCHLORIC ACID
C_6H_6 + Cl_2 → C_6H_5Cl + HCl

SECOND STEP

CHLOROBENZENE + CAUSTIC SODA → SODIUM PHENATE + SODIUM CHLORIDE + WATER
C_6H_5Cl + 2 NaOH → C_6H_5ONa + NaCl + H_2O

THIRD STEP

SODIUM PHENATE + HYDROCHLORIC ACID → PHENOL + SODIUM CHLORIDE
C_6H_5ONa + HCl → C_6H_5OH + NaCl

Figure 4-6. Chemistry of phenol via the chlorination process.

is then electrolyzed to form additional caustic and chlorine.

The chemistry of these three steps is shown in Figure 4-6; the flow sheet is shown in Figure 4-7. The hydrolysis takes place at 4,000 to 5,000 psi at about 700° F. Corrosive materials must be handled.

Sulfonation Process. The four stages of this process are: (1) Benzene is reacted with sulfuric acid to form benzene sulfonic acid. (2) The benzene sulfonic acid is converted to the sodium benzenesulfonate (NaBS) by reaction with sodium sulfite. (3) Caustic fusion of the sodium benzene-

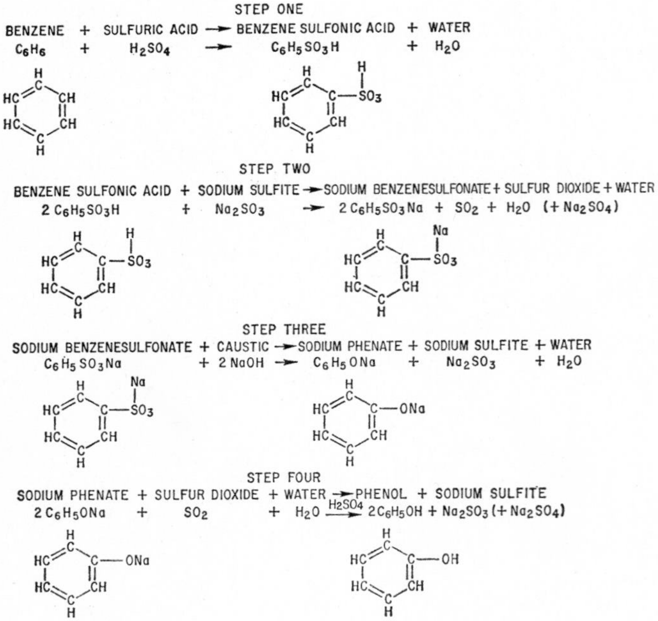

Figure 4-8. Chemistry of phenol via the sulfonation process.

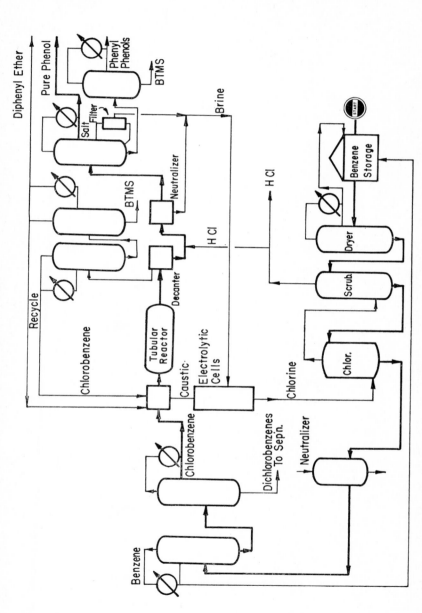

Figure 4-7. Phenol can be made from benzene and chlorine using this chlorination or chlorobenzene process.

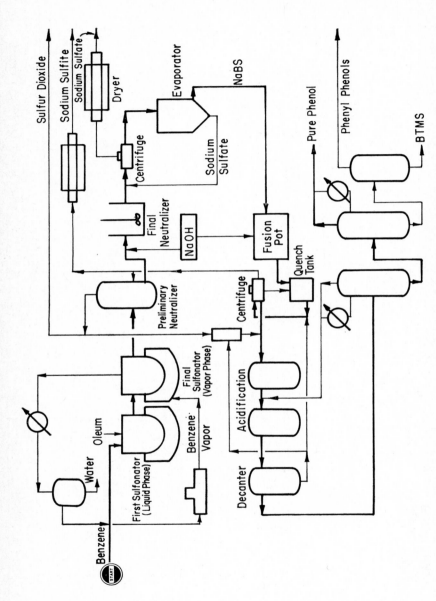

Figure 4-9. Use this arrangement for phenol by the sulfonation process.

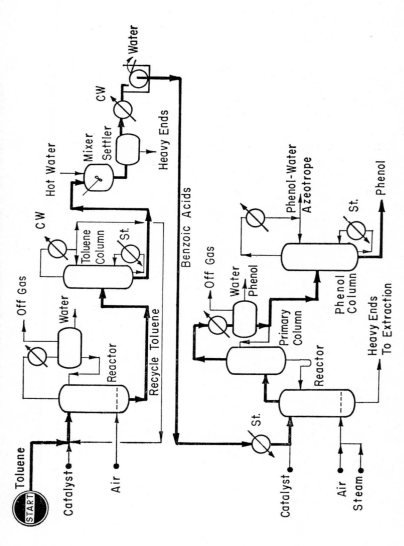

Figure 4-10. Phenol is produced from toluene via benzoic acid in this arrangement.

sulfonate produces sodium phenate. (4) The sodium
phenate is acidified with sulfur dioxide (and a small
amount of sulfuric acid) to form phenol. The final purification of the phenol is done in a series of three columns.
The chemistry of these reactions is shown in Figure
4-8; the flow sheet is shown in Figure 4-9. Large quantities of sodium sulfite and sodium sulfate are made as
byproducts in the process. Some special materials of construction must be used to combat corrosion.

Other Process Routes. There are two other processes
practiced commercially in the United States:

1. Phenol from toluene. Dow has a small plant (40
million pounds/year) in the United States and two in
foreign countries using this process. A flow diagram is
shown in Figure 4-10; details of the operation have
been published.[2]

2. Schenectady Chemical has a benzene oxidation process in operation (20 million pounds/year) but little has
been published about it.

One other process which deserves mentioning is the
manufacture of phenol from benzene via cyclohexane
oxidation (refer to Figure 4-11) ; two of these plants have
been installed abroad.

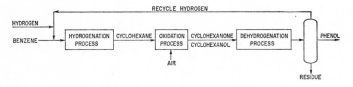

Figure 4-11. Hydrogenating benzene to cyclohexane which can be
oxidized to produce phenol

TABLE 4-1—U.S. Phenol Producers

Company	Location	Process	Phenol Capacity – millions of lbs/yr.
Allied[6]	Philadelphia, Pa.	Cumene	200
Chevron	Richmond, Calif.	Cumene	50
Clark Oil	Chicago, Ill.	Cumene	30
Dow	Kalama, Wash.	Toluene	40
	Midland, Mich.	Chlorobenzene (Chlorination)	230
Hercules[6]	Gibbstown, N. J.	Cumene	30
Hooker	South Shore, Ky.	Modified Raschig	65
	Tonawanda, N. Y.	Modified Raschig	65
Monsanto	Alvin, Texas	Cumene	140
	Monsanto, Ill.	Sulfonation	115
Reichhold	Tuscaloosa, Ala.	Sulfonation	90
Schenectady	Rotterdam Jct., N.Y.	Benzene Oxidation	20
Shell	Houston, Texas	Cumene	50
Skelly	El Dorado, Kan.	Cumene	50
Union Carbide	Marietta, Ohio	Modified Raschig	110

Total — Synthetic.. 1285
Total — Natural Phenol.. 60

GRAND TOTAL — SYNTHETIC AND NATURAL............ 1345

Capacity to be added in 1966:

Allied	Philadelphia, Pa.	Cumene	100
Union Carbide	Bound Brook, N. J.	Cumene	150

Total — to be added in 1966............................... 250
GRAND TOTAL — SYNTHETIC AND NATURAL in 1966..... 1,595

Approximate raw-material requirements for one pound of phenol:

PROCESS ROUTE	POUNDS OF RAW MATERIALS					
	Benzene	Propylene	HCl	Cl2	Caustic	H2SO4
Cumene	1.16	0.65				
Raschig	1.1		0.2			
Chlorobenzene (Chlorination)	1.18		0.5*	1.1**	1.37**	
Sulfonation	1.0				1.7	1.75

*This material is obtained as a byproduct in the chlorination step.
**Much of this material is obtained from an electrolysis cell operated as part of the plant.

U.S. Phenol Producers.

A list of U.S. phenol producers is shown in Table 4-1. The economics of phenol manufacture are discussed in a separate section.

TABLE 4-2—Markets for U.S. Phenol—1965 and 1970

	Millions of Pounds	
	1965	1970
Phenolic resins............................	590	810
Bisphenol A................................	90	140
Alkylated phenols.........................	80	80
Caprolactam...............................	80	90
Adipic acid................................	50	60
Petroleum refining........................	45	50
Plasticizers...............................	40	60
2,4 D Acids................................	30	35
Pentachlorophenol.........................	30	35
Exports....................................	45	35
Miscellaneous.............................	70	70
Totals...............................	1.180[5]	1,500[5]

MARKETS

The markets for U.S. phenol are projected to grow about 5 percent[5] a year over the next five years, from an estimated 1,180 million pounds[5] in 1965 to 1,500 million pounds[5] in 1970.

Phenol consumption is divided into 10 major domestic outlets and only one—phenolic resins—accounts for a sizable percentage of phenol output (refer Table 4-2 and Figure 4-12). This wide diversification of phenol demand will prevent it from showing outstanding growth; at the same time this widespread demand offers a degree of protection against market setbacks. Each of the phenol outlets is discussed briefly below.

Phenolic Resins. These materials for years have dominated the phenol markets and will continue to do so in the future. In 1965 they will account for 50 percent of the consumption of U.S. phenol, or 590 million pounds. This consumption will increase to 54 percent of phenol consumption or 810 million pounds by 1970.

The phenolic resin market in turn is divided among many uses as shown in the tabulation below. The growth rate of the phenolic resin market is expected to be about

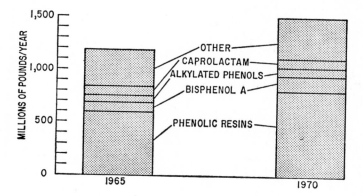

Figure 4-12. U.S. markets for phenol should follow this trend

6 to 7 percent over the next five years; the various segments of this market are marked "+" if they are growing faster than the average phenolic-resin growth rate and "—" if they are growing slower than average:

Item	% of Phenolic Resin Market in 1965	Relative Growth
Molding Materials	30	—
Bonding and adhesive resins for:		
Laminating	14	—
Thermal insulation	13	—
Plywood	12	+
Foundry or shell molding	8	+
Friction materials	4	+
Coated and bonded abrasives	3	+
Fibrous and granulated wood	3	—
Other bonding and adhesive uses	4	—
Protective coatings	4	—
Other uses	5	—
	100%	

Even though some of the items listed in the above table are growing less than the average growth for phenolic resins, all are showing absolute growth. A few of the more important markets are discussed below.

Molding materials. These materials are used in the following:

Electrical devices, such as panel boards and switch gear	43%
Appliance knobs and handles	23%
Bottle caps	6%
Washing machine agitators	5%
Automobile parts	5%
Telephones	5%
Miscellaneous	13%
	100%

The electrical and appliance markets are expected to continue to expand. New injection molding machines that speed up the molding cycle by a factor of up to 10 times were first introduced in 1963; these machines plus several improved resins have contributed to increased consumption of molding resins. The markets for molding resins are expected to grow at slightly less than the over-all growth rate for phenolic resins, although they will continue to be the largest phenol outlet in the resin category for the foreseeable future.

Plywood. The bonding of plywood represents the most rapidly growing outlet for phenolic resins; consumption of phenolic resins in this application has increased 48 percent in the last two years to an expected total of 106 million pounds in 1965. Phenolics may capture the entire market for bonding all softwood plies, and plywood usage as a whole will grow more rapidly than the construction industry.

Other. Foundry moldings and coated and bonded abrasives have increased phenolic resin consumption by about 40 percent each in the last two years while friction materials, such as brake linings and clutch facings, have increased about 20 percent. All other outlets are growing at less than the 6 to 7 percent a year rate averaged by the phenolic resin market. This market will continue to be characterized by wide diversification.

Bisphenol A. This is a rapidly growing market because of its consumption in polycarbonates and epoxy resins. Polycarbonates are a relatively low-volume outlet but are expected to grow rapidly. Epoxy resins are presently widely used in coating, potting and encapsulating. The growth rate of bisphenol A is projected to be between 9 and 10 percent yearly through 1970. However, because of the dominance of phenolic resins in phenol's over-all market picture, bisphenol A will still account for less than 10 percent of phenol consumption in 1970.

Alkylated Phenols. These chemicals, specifically nonyl phenol and dodecyl phenol, are used in oil well additives and rubber chemicals and plastics; and these markets are expected to grow. However, they are also used in detergents, and this outlet is expected to decrease because of the introduction of biodegradable detergents. In summary, alkylated phenol production should about remain constant over the next five years and thereby account for 5 percent of phenol consumption in 1970 versus almost 7 percent in 1965.

Caprolactam. This is the monomer for Nylon 6 and Nylon 6 markets are growing rapidly. However, Allied is the only U.S. company making caprolactam from phenol as the other two manufacturers use cyclohexane as a raw material. Accurate comparative economics have not been published but it appears that the cyclohexane route is cheaper. Therefore, over the long run little growth is projected for phenol in this market. It will account for 7 percent of phenol consumption in 1965 and 6 percent in 1970.

Other. No other outlet accounts for as much as 5 percent of phenol consumption; this will still be the case in 1970. These other outlets are in adipic acid, petroleum refining, plasticizers, 2, 4-D acids, pentachlorophenol salicylates, exports, and miscellaneous. Consumption in plasticizers will grow at an annual rate of 8 to 9 percent and represents the fastest growing area in this general category. As a whole this "other" category will account for 340 million pounds of phenol consumption in 1965, or 29 percent of the total; in 1970 the comparative figures will be 380 million pounds, or 25 percent of the total. A projected slight drop in exports is one of the factors contributing to a relatively slow growth in this "other" category.

INDIVIDUAL COMPANIES

Dow and Monsanto have historically been the largest producers of phenol and they continue in that role today. Each has about 20 percent of the total U.S. capacity with Dow's capacity being 270 million pounds/year and Monsanto's 265 pounds/year. Allied is the third largest with 200 million pounds, or 15 percent of U.S. capacity; but will be first on the completion in 1966 of a new 100 million pound plant—that is unless Dow or Monsanto expands. The remainder of the capacity is split among nine other companies, none of whom has over 10 percent of U.S. capacity.

Most of the phenol manufacturers have some internal use for phenol, refer Table 4-3. In the case of the chemical companies such as Dow, Monsanto and Allied, the internal uses are substantial; on the other hand, the internal uses in Clark Oil and Skelly Oil are insignificant. Approximately one half of total U.S. output is

TABLE 4-3—Captive Uses by Companies Manufacturing Phenol

Manufacturer	Captive Uses by Companies Manufacturing Phenol									
	Phenolic Resins	Bisphenol A	Alkylated Phenols	Caprolactam	Adipic Acid	Petroleum Refining	Plasticizers	2, 4D Acids	Pentachlorophenol	Salicylates
Allied.........	X				X		X			
Chevron........	X			X		X				
Clark Oil......						X				
Dow............		X				X	X	X	X	X
Hercules.......								X		
Hooker.........	X									
Monsanto.......	X	X	X		X	X	X	X	X	X
Reichold.......	X						X		X	
Schenectady....	X									
Shell..........		X				X				
Skelly.........						X				
Union Carbide..	X	X	X				X			

Basic Reference Source: U.S. Tariff Commission

TABLE 4-4—Historical Data—U.S. Production, Number of Producers, and Sales Value of Phenol

Year	No. of Producers of Synthetic Phenol	PRODUCTION Millions of Pounds/Year Total	Natural	Synthetic Total	Cumene	Other	Sales millions of Lbs./Year	Avg. Price c/lb. Price	Total Value of Production millions of dollars
1953	7	382	26	356	0	356	200	17	65
1954	8	418	21	397	0	397	219	14	59
1955	8	517	42	475	70	405	280	15	78
1956	9	549	40	509	94	415	303	16	87
1957	9	556	42	514	101	413	289	16	89
1958	9	506	43	463	99	364	281	16	81
1959	10	692	40	652	138	514	414	14	97
1960	10	773	42	731	173	558	424	14	108
1961	10	779	48	731	189	542	334	14	109
1962	10	826	52	774	234	540	387	12	99
1963	11	935	51	884	325	559	480	9.5	89
1964	13	113	50	1063	444	619	493	9.7	108
1965*	13	1225	51	1174	520	654	500	9.5	116
1966*	—	1700	51	1649	949	700	540	8.5–9.5	114–161

Source: U.S. Tariff Commission.
*Estimates.

consumed internally and one half sold. It is believed that all of the producers are major sellers of phenol.

There are many purchasers of phenol in the United States. For example, there are well over 50 manufacturers of phenolic resins; this outlet consumes 50 percent of U.S. phenol output. Thus some of these 50 companies purchase large quantities of phenol. As there are many buyers of phenol, a widespread sales and distribution system is needed. Skelly solved this problem by arranging for R. W. Greeff & Co. to handle their marketing.

HISTORICAL DATA

Table 4-4 presents data based on U.S. Tariff Commission reports for 1953 through 1964 and on the author's estimates for 1965 and 1970.

These data show a gradual rise in phenol output, at a growth rate of about 9 percent over the last five years (refer Table 4-4 and Figure 4-13). The important

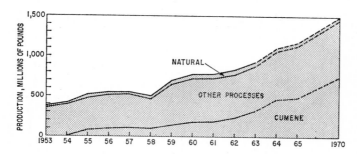

Figure 4-13. Production pattern of phenol in the U.S., 1953-1970

new trend has been the move toward manufacture of phenol from cumene; cumene-based phenol has increased from zero in 1954 up to 43 percent of total phenol output in 1965.

The price of phenol has dropped from 16¢/pound in the 1956-59 period to today's posted price of 11.25¢, although the 1965 average sales price will be about 9.5¢ which is the same as was actually received in 1963. Refer to Figure 4-14. This price drop has resulted in the value of phenol production in 1965 being about $112 million dollars, or about the same as in 1960. Production in 1965 will be 50 percent greater than in 1960. Refer to Figure 4-15.

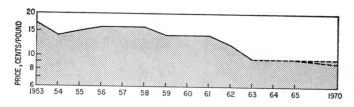

Figure 4-14. Sales value of U.S. phenol has steadily declined and leveled off in 1963

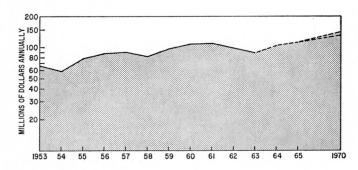

Figure 4-15. Total value of U.S. phenol production has increased
gradually since 1953

The number of producers has gradually increased
through the years although it has increased only from
10 up to 12 in the last six years.

ECONOMICS

It is difficult to make accurate economic comparisons
between the various routes because of the special factors
inherent in each process route:

1. The cumene process depends on realizing substantial byproduct credits for the acetone, which is about
40 percent by weight of the plant output.

2. The Raschig process has higher capital costs than
the other ones, and therefore must be built on a large-
scale basis.

3. The chlorination (chlorobenzene) process depends
on the electrolysis of byproduct sodium chloride to produce chlorine and caustic, which are used in the process;
therefore, it requires a low-cost power source.

4. The sulfonation process produces large quantities of
sodium sulfite and sodium sulfate, which are relatively
low in value and therefore require nearby markets.

Little has been published about the economics of the toluene route or the cyclohexane-oxidation route.

However, it is possible to draw the conclusion that the cumene route will account for most of the future expansion in U.S. phenol capacity. Several items point to this:

1. Monsanto recently built a cumene-based phenol plant at Alvin, Texas, and in so doing shut down a small sulfonation plant at Avon, Calif. Monsanto continues to operate a large sulfonation plant at Monsanto, Ill. The significant point is that Monsanto, a major manufacturer of sulfuric acid with long experience with the sulfonation route, selected the cumene route rather than the sulfonation route.

2. Union Carbide, with a 110 million pound/year Raschig plant, has decided to build a new 150 million pound/year plant using the cumene process.

3. Dow, a long-time manufacturer via the chlorobenzene route and a major manufacturer of chlorine, built its most recent plant using its new toluene-based route. The cumene route is licensed by at least two companies and therefore is available to a manufacturer who wishes to add phenol capacity. On the other hand, only Dow has the toluene-route knowhow and it has not yet licensed this knowhow to another company.

Therefore, an analysis of the economics of manufacturing phenol via the cumene route will provide an insight to the possible future price level of phenol.

Allied has the largest capacity of any cumene-based producer and its process is being used by both Clark Oil and Skelly Oil; however, details of the economics of the Allied process are not readily available. A U.O.P. process to make cumene from benzene and propylene is available and is similar to the process to make ethylbenzene from benzene and ethylene. The cumene process to phenol is similar in complexity to making styrene from ethylbenzene. It is believed reasonable to assume that capital and operating costs to make phenol and acetone from benzene and propylene are comparable to those to make styrene from benzene and ethylene. Therefore, the analysis which follows is on this basic assumption, with the unit output of styrene equated with the combined outputs of phenol and acetone. A further indication of the reasonableness of this approach is that the capital costs of a phenol plant recently built by I.C.I. in England are in line with the capital costs used below.

Basis: 130 million pounds/year of phenol
78 million pounds/year of acetone
U. S. Gulf Coast Location
Battery Limits Capital = $10 million or 7.7¢/annual pound of phenol.
Offsite Capital at 33% of B. L. = $ 3.3 million

Total Capital $13.3 million or
10.2¢/annual pound of phenol.

Direct Operating Costs = 2.4¢/pound of phenol
(or 1.5¢/pound of phenol and acetone combined)
Return on Investment = 20% before taxes
Sales and Admin. Overhead = 1¢/pound of phenol

The table below shows the effect of benzene value.

	All figures in ¢/pound of phenol except the phenol base prices	
Benzene price, ¢/gallon	25	28
Raw material cost—benzene	4.0	4.3
—propylene at 2.3¢/lb.	1.5	1.5
Byproduct credit—acetone at 4.6¢/lb.	—2.8	—2.8
Net raw material cost	2.7	3.0
Direct operating costs	2.4	2.4
Subtotal: out of pocket costs	5.1	5.4
Depreciation, at 10% of B. L. Plant	0.8	0.8
Subtotal: Breakeven costs	5.9	6.2

Return on investment, at 20%	2.0	2.0
Subtotal without sales and admin.	7.9	8.2
Sales and admin. overhead	1.0	1.0
Grand Total	8.9	9.2

Although the above figures are only approximations, the fact that raw material costs are significant components of the over-all cost helps the accuracy of the final totals. However, there are indications that the direct operating costs and capital-related costs shown above are higher than would actually be realized.[4]

In addition to the variation in benzene value, variation in sales value of acetone also has a major effect on the plant profitability (refer to Figure 4-16).

With raw material costs in the ranges shown above, it can be concluded that a sale value of about 9¢/

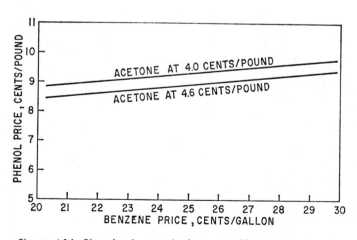

Figure 4-16. Phenol price required to earn 20 percent return on investment before taxes using the cumene process

pound is required to justify the construction of a new phenol plant. Any extra distribution costs incurred in delivering phenol to many small customers would be an additional expense.

The importance of large-scale operation is indicated by the fact that a 50 million pound/year plant would require 1½ to 2¢/pound more revenue to earn the same return on investment as a 130 million pound per year plant.

THE FUTURE

Phenol consumption will continue its steady but unspectacular growth. Any losses phenol suffers in one market will be more than offset by gains in other markets. It will continue to enjoy a very wide diversification of uses.

Phenolic resins will account for a slightly greater portion of phenol consumption in the future. The fact that there are many makers of phenolic resins places a premium on the importance of a good distribution system. This in turn makes it more difficult for a newcomer to enter the phenol manufacturing business; thus most of the future expansion will be one of the following three cases:

1. Addition of new plants or expansion of existing plants by present manufacturers.

2. Installation of cumene-manufacturing facilities by petroleum refiners, who then in turn would sell the cumene to a chemical company for conversion to phenol.

3. Installation of cumene and phenol manufacturing facilities by a petroleum refiner, who would then conclude a marketing arrangement with a chemical distributor.

Most of the future growth in capacity will be via the cumene route. The economics of this route depend to a considerable extent on the sales value of the byproduct acetone. The following table summarizes the acetone supply situation in the United States.

Year	Production in Millions of Pounds		Cumene Route as a % of Total	Sales in Millions of Pounds		Cumene Route as a % of Total
	Total	From Cumene		Total	From Cumene	
1963	943	196	21	537	128	24
1965	1090	294	27	620	192	31
1970	1450	428	30	830	280	34

Thus, acetone from cumene will increase as a percentage of total acetone produced from about 27 percent in 1965 to 30 percent in 1970. Most of the remaining acetone is manufactured from isopropanol. The manufacturers making phenol from cumene do not have as much internal consumption of acetone as do those who make acetone from isopropanol. Hence, the acetone from cumene will account for 31 percent of total acetone sales in 1965 and is expected to account for 34 percent by 1970. Acetone from cumene is produced as a byproduct and therefore must be sold at whatever price it will bring.

The fact that this byproduct material will account for an increasingly-larger amount of the total acetone sold will continue to put pressure on the acetone sales price. In 1963 the average price of acetone was 5.0¢/pound for material produced from isopropanol and only 4.6c/pound for all other acetone, most of which came from cumene-based phenol producers. These average sales prices were down from the 1962 averages of 5.9¢ and 4.8¢, respectively. The difference between 4.6¢/pound and a value of 4.0¢/pound would represent about 0.4¢/pound of phenol.

From the discussion on "economics" and Figure 4-16, it can be concluded that as long as benzene remains in the 25¢ to 28¢/gallon range, then phenol price required to justify a new 130 million pound/year cumene-based phenol plant would be 8.9¢ to 9.6¢/pound with acetone varying between 4.6¢ and 4.0¢/pound.

As most new phenol plants will be based on cumene and some will be larger than 130 million pounds/year, future average sales value for phenol is expected to vary between the 9.5¢/pound projected for 1965 to possibly as low as 8.9¢/pound. One of the major determining factors will be the future value of U.S. benzene, which in turn will be affected by the U.S. Government's action on the requests for import quotas for Puerto Rican plants and Foreign-Trade Zones.[7]

Another important point, although of less importance than benzene and acetone sales values, is the future value of propylene to a refiner. This is not expected to change radically; however, it will be the subject of another study.

If phenol sales price is between 8.9¢ and 9.5¢/pound then the total value of phenol produced in the United States in 1970 will be $133 to $142 million with total production of 1,500[5] million pounds. Refer to Figure 4-14.

Literature Cited

1. Gordon, Joseph, "What Are The Processes and Prospects for Phenol?" *Hydrocarbon Processing & Petroleum Refiner,* 40: 193-206, June 1961.

2. "Phenol from Toluene," *Hydrocarbon Processing & Petroleum Refiner,* 40:280, November 1961.

3. Sources such as *Hydrocarbon Processing & Petroleum Refiner; Oil, Paint and Drug Reporter; Chemical Engineering; Oil and Gas Journal; Chemical Week;* and *Chemical Engineering News* were used for news items and market and capacity estimates. However, the author takes full responsibility for the final estimates published.

4. "Hooker and Cumene Phenol Costs Compared," *European Chemical News,* 4:29, November 29, 1963.

5. Tariff Commission preliminary reports show 1965 production as 1.225 billion pounds. Table 4-4 has been revised for 1965 and 1970.

6. These companies have added or are adding additional capacity as of mid-1966.

7. See Reference 1, Chapter 5.

5

Toluene

SOME 95 PERCENT of U.S. toluene is obtained from petroleum and this percentage will increase in the future. The consumption of extracted toluene will rise at the rate of about 6 percent a year to a 1970 figure of 750 million gallons, compared with 552 million gallons in 1965. The use of toluene in dealkylation units to make benzene was the major consumer of toluene in 1965 and is expected to grow in importance, so that by 1970 toluene consumption in this market will account for 64 percent of all extracted toluene versus only 43 percent in 1965. The total production of toluene in the United States is between 3 and 3½ billion gallons annually and most of this remains unextracted in the gasoline pool.

As toluene is extracted as a byproduct of benzene and/or xylene operations, it is valued by refiners on an "alternate-use" basis. As the alternate use is in the motor gasoline pool, it is sold at a price high enough to pay for marketing costs plus yield a small profit. Manufacturers have been realizing about 17¢/gallon for toluene, and the future sales value is expected to remain in the 16¢ to 18¢/gallon range. Toluene is sold in the major-consuming areas away from the Gulf Coast for 19¢ to 23¢/gallon depending on whether it is delivered or at a terminal, and of course, depending on the quantity involved.

There are slightly over 30 petroleum manufacturers of toluene, with the largest producing about 10 percent of the nation's output; there are many more buyers of toluene and this large number of buyers and sellers results in a very competitive market. Also it places a premium on the necessity of having a good distribution system. The production of toluene has been climbing steadily, but price drops have restricted the climb of total value of toluene produced. However, it is expected that the value of toluene produced will pass the $100 million mark by 1967 or 1968. The future production and price level of toluene rests to some extent on the future action of the U. S. Government on requests to establish aromatics plants in Puerto Rico and export byproduct gasoline to the United States and on the requests to establish Foreign-Trade Zones in the United States based on utilizing low-cost foreign naphtha as feedstock.[1]

MANUFACTURE

Toluene is obtained from two main sources:

Petroleum	96%
Coal tar and coke-oven light oils	4%
	100%

Most of the toluene obtained from petroleum is obtained from reformers in petroleum refineries. Some is obtained as a byproduct from styrene monomer plants but this amount is of minor importance compared with the production from refineries.

Approximately 90 percent of the toluene obtained from

coal tar and coke-oven light oils comes from the coke-oven light oils. Toluene is present in these light oils in an approximate ratio of:

$$
\begin{aligned}
\text{Benzene} &= 15 \\
\text{Toluene} &= 4 \\
\text{Xylenes} &= 1
\end{aligned}
$$

This compares with the ratios from a catalytic reformer in a petroleum refiner as follows:

$$
\begin{aligned}
\text{Benzene} &= 1 \\
\text{Toluene} &= 2\frac{1}{2} \text{ to } 3 \\
\text{Xylenes and ethylbenzene} &= 2 \text{ to } 2\frac{1}{2}
\end{aligned}
$$

This composition of the feed streams is the reason why the percentage of U.S. toluene produced from coal tar and coke-oven light oils is only 4 percent while the corresponding figure for benzene is 15 percent.

The basic principles involved in production of toluene from coal tar and coke-oven light oils is the same as that in recovering it from the reformate from a petroleum-refinery reformer; therefore, since the production of by-product toluene from styrene monomer plants is very small, only the manufacturer of toluene from petroleum refinery reformers will be discussed.

Toluene from Refinery Reformate. Most refineries have a reforming operation that converts naphthenes into aromatics in order to increase the octane number of the gasoline pool. In cases in which the refiner does not wish to extract the aromatics to use or sell for chemical purposes then he typically will reform the C_7 and C_8 naphthenes; in this case he does not separate the C_7 aromatics from the C_8 aromatics but will use the mixture in his gasoline pool. Thus, he will not be a producer of chemical-grade toluene but rather will be a producer of a blending stock for his gasoline pool.

However, in those cases in which the refiner wishes

to manufacture benzene for chemical purposes, he will reform his C_6, C_7 and C_8 naphthenes into aromatics; will extract the aromatics from the remaining hydrocarbons; and will separate the aromatics into the various components needed for his requirements as determined by his marketing capabilities and his gasoline pool. In this case he may dump a combined C_7 and C_8 stream into the gasoline pool after having removed the benzene, or alternately may separate the C_7 and C_8 materials and sell part or all of the toluene and xylenes in the chemical and solvents markets, with any remainder being used in the gasoline pool.

There are five steps in the manufacture of toluene from refinery reformate; these are shown in Figure 5-1. The chemistry is shown in Figure 5-2.

These five main steps are:

1. A straight-run gasoline fraction (100°-390° F ASTM) is treated to remove sulfur; the need for this treatment varies with the character of the crude oil.

2. The C_6, C_7 and C_8 heart cut (150°-300° F ASTM) is separated from the heavier and lighter materials by distillation.

3. Naphthenes are converted to aromatics by reforming over a platinum catalyst.

4. Aromatics are separated from paraffins and residual naphthenes by dissolving in a solvent, such as sulfolane or diethylene glycol, and then in turn stripping the aromatics from the solvent. Figure 5-3 shows a process which utilizes sulfolane as the extraction agent.

5. The final step is the separation of the aromatics stream into benzene, toluene, and xylenes; following a clay treatment, the combined stream goes to a series of columns where benzene goes overhead from the first column, toluene overhead from the second, and xylenes overhead from the third.

The economics of these operations are discussed in a separate section.

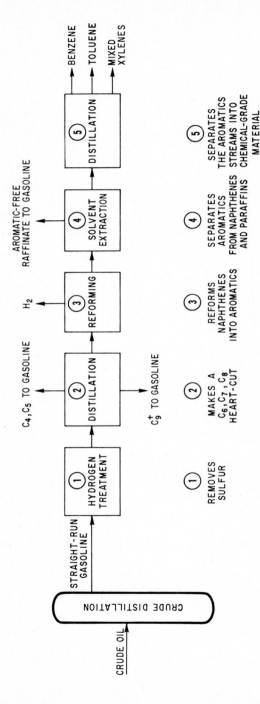

Figure 5-1. Typical processing scheme for obtaining toluene from a petroleum refinery

TYPICAL REACTIONS

(I) DIMETHYLCYCLOPENTANE ⟶ TOLUENE + HYDROGEN

C_7H_{14} ⟶ C_7H_8 + $3H_2$

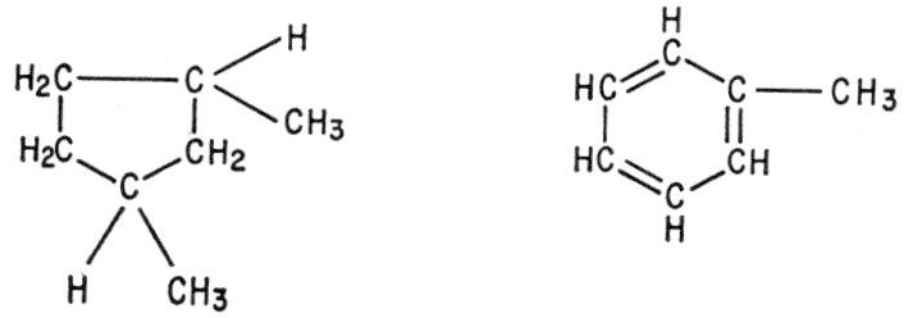

(2) METHYLCYCLOHEXANE ⟶ TOLUENE + HYDROGEN

C_7H_{14} ⟶ C_7H_8 + $3H_2$

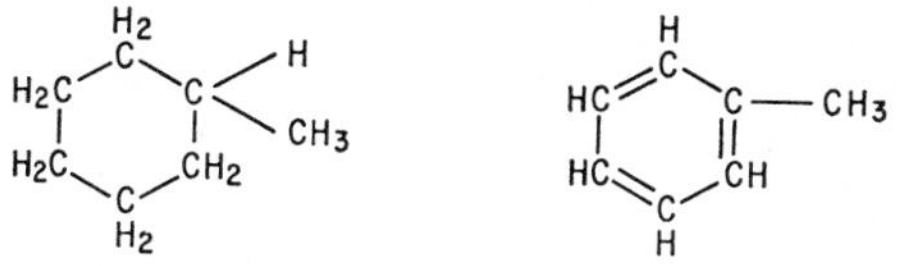

Figure 5-2. Chemistry of toluene manufacture from napthenes by reforming

U.S. Toluene Producers. Those U.S. companies producing toluene from petroleum feedstocks are listed in Table 5-1. The capacities included in this list are those which represent the capacity of the toluene extraction and separation facilities. There will be 3 to 3½ billion gallons of toluene produced this year by reforming but only one-sixth of this will be extracted; the remainder will go into gasoline without having been extracted.

MARKETS

Toluene consumption can be divided into two categories: (1) End-uses, such as chemicals, aviation gasoline, and solvents, which require toluene; and (2) motor gasoline, which takes the toluene produced in excess of the toluene required in the end-uses just mentioned.

TABLE 5-1—U.S. Toluene Producers from Petroleum Feedstock

Company	Location	Toluene Capacity—millions of gallons/year
Amoco[3]	Texas City, Tex.	20
Ashland	N Tonawanda, N.Y.	8
	Catlettsburg, Ky.	11
AtlanticRichfield	Wilmington, Calif.	24
Chevron	El Segundo, Calif.	24
	Richmond, Calif.	8
Cosden	Big Spring, Tex.	15
Crown Central	Houston, Tex.	10
Dow	Bay City, Mich.	17
Enjay[3]	Baton Rouge, La.	15
	Baytown, Tex.	50
Gulf[3]	Philadelphia, Pa.	15
	Port Arthur, Tex.	5
Hess	Corpus Christi, Tex.	18
Leonard	Mount Pleasant, Mich.	3
Marathon	Texas City, Tex.	12
Mobil	Beaumont, Tex.	25
Monsanto	Alvin, Tex.	32
Pontiac	Corpus Christi, Tex.	13
Shell[3]	Houston, Tex.	30
	Odessa, Tex.	10
	Wilmington, Calif.	10
	Wood River, Ill.	15
Signal	Houston, Tex.	16
Sinclair	Houston, Tex.	20
	Marcus Hook, Pa.	6
South Hampton	Silsbee, Tex.	6
Sun	Marcus Hook, Pa.	25
Sunray DX	Tulsa, Okla.	4
Suntide	Corpus Christi, Tex.	13
Tenneco	Chalmette, La.	8
Texaco[3]	Port Arthur, Tex.	20
Union Carbide[3]	South Charleston, W. Va.	10
Union Oil-Atlantic	Nederland, Tex.	20
Union Oil	Lemont, Ill.	10
Vickers	Potwin, Kan.	5

Total from Petroleum Operations	554
Total from Styrene Monomer Operations	15
Total from Coke-Oven Producers and Tar Distillers	50
Grand Total	619

Capacity expected to be added during 1966/1967:

Company	Location	
Cities Service	Lake Charles, La.	36
Coastal States	Corpus Christi, Tex.	10
Southwestern	Corpus Christi, Tex.	10
Texaco	Port Arthur, Tex.	11
Subtotal—for 1966/67		67
Grand Total, all U.S. capacity end of 1967		686

NOTES:
1. The above estimates are approximate. The possible output from coke ovens and tar distillers depends on the output of the steel industry. The output of some of the petroleum refiners can be boosted substantially with little or no new capital investment.
2. Continental Oil, Phillips and Velsicol are listed by the U.S. Tariff Commission as being toluene producers; their outputs are believed to be relatively small.

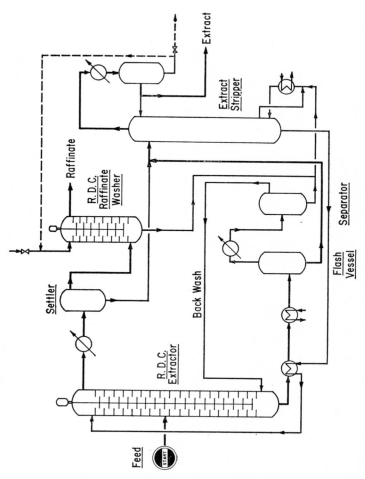

Figure 5-3. Scheme for extracting aromatics from refinery reformate

TABLE 5-2—Markets for U.S. Toluene, 1965 and 1970

	Millions of Gallons	
	1965	1970
Benzene (HDA units)	230	480
Solvents	50	64
Miscellaneous chemicals	40	62
Aviation gasoline	35	35
Exports	30	10
Toluene diisocyanate	12	23
TNT	10	10
Phenol	7	14
Sulfates	6	7
Toluene Demand: Avgas, chemicals, & solvents	420	705
Toluene Production	552[2]	750
Difference = amount used in motor gasoline pool =	132	45

The end-uses requiring toluene are projected to grow approximately 11 percent a year between 1965 and 1970; thus these end-uses will consume 705 million gallons of toluene in 1970 versus 420 in 1965. On the other hand, total toluene production is not expected to increase at this pace as much of the benzene used in the United States in 1970 will come from hydrodealkylation (HDA) of toluene. Accordingly, rather than toluene's being produced as a byproduct of benzene production it will actually be consumed in the production of benzene. In line with this, the amount of toluene which is dumped into the motor gasoline pools will decline from an estimated 132 million gallons in 1965 to maybe 45 million gallons in 1970; this latter number is very dependent on the process route selected by the companies which will be adding benzene capacity in the next five years. Also it will be affected by the action of the U.S. Government on the requests for import quotas for Puerto Rican operations and Foreign-Trade Zones in the United States.[1]

Additionally, these figures on the consumption of toluene do not include an estimated 2½ to 3 billion gallons of

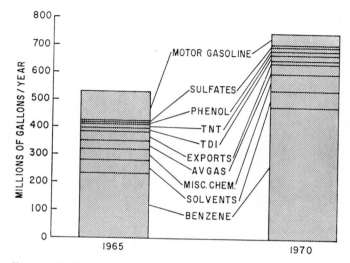

Figure 5-4. U.S. consumption pattern for toluene, 1965 and 1970

toluene which is consumed in the nation's gasoline pool without having been extracted. Table 5-2.

If the above numbers are correct then the amount of toluene extracted in 1970 will be about 750 million gallons, or a growth rate of about 6 percent annually from the 1965 base of 552 million gallons.[2]

The use of larger amounts of toluene as feed to HDA units will be the major factor accounting for toluene's rapid growth, refer to Figure 5-4. This along with other outlets will be discussed below.

Benzene (HDA Units). The HDA units, which were either shutdown or running at partial capacity just a few years ago, are now running near capacity; they consumed about 230 million gallons in 1965 and are expected

TABLE 5-3—U.S. Producers of Benzene from Toluene

Company	Location	Benzene Capacity— millions of gallons/year	Estimated Toluene Consumption in 1965— millions of gallons*
Ashland...........	Catlettsburg, Ky.	6	7
Bethlehem........	Sparrows Point, Md.	8	9
Cosden[3]..........	Big Spring, Tex.	20	2**
Crown Central....	Houston, Tex.	13	15
Dow..............	Bay City, Mich.	13	15
	Freeport, Tex.	30	35
Enjay[3]...........	Baytown, Tex.	30	35
Gulf..............	Philadelphia, Pa.	12	14
Monsanto........	Alvin, Tex.	25	29
Shell.............	Odessa, Tex.	15	17
Signal............	Houston, Tex.	12	14
South Hampton...	Silsbee, Tex.	6	7
Sunray DX........	Tulsa, Okla.	12	14
Suntide..........	Corpus Christi, Tex.	15	17
Total..........		217	230

* Based on 1.25 gallons of toluene per gallon of benzene; all companies assumed to be operating at capacity with nominal allowance for downtime.
** Started up late 1965.

to consume as much as 480 million gallons in 1970. There will be an estimated 350 million gallons annually more of U.S. benzene consumed in 1970 than in 1965. It is not known how much of this will be based on toluene but the amount will primarily be affected by the U.S. Government's actions on requests for quotas enabling refiners in Puerto Rico to import gasoline into the United States and on requests for Foreign-Trade Zones allowing companies to import low-cost foreign naphtha.[1]

The estimate of 1970 toluene consumption is based on the assumption that 50 percent or more of the additional U.S. benzene capacity will be based on toluene.

About 100 gallons of toluene are required to produce 80 gallons of benzene via this dealkylation process. Producers of benzene from toluene are listed in Table 5-3; also shown is an estimate of their 1965 toluene consumption.

Solvents. Toluene is used in a variety of solvent applications, with nitrocellulose lacquers probably the largest single outlet. This use in solvents should represent a steady growth of 5 percent annually over the next five years; thus 1970 comsumption will be 64 million gallons versus 50 million gallons in 1965.

Miscellaneous Chemicals. Included in this category are such uses as benzoic acid, benzaldehyde, benzyl chloride and vinyl toluene. A possible consumer of U.S. toluene in the future will be terephthalic acid; this is now made in the United States from paraxylene but Mitsubishi in Japan has been operating a plant longer than two years using toluene as a raw material. This miscellaneous category is expected to consume 62 million gallons of toluene in 1970 versus 40 million in 1965.

Aviation Gasoline. The volume of toluene used in this market is not expected to change substantially in the years just ahead.

Exports. These are expected to drop somewhat as more aromatics plants are built abroad.

Toluene Diisocyanate. Rapid growth is projected for this chemical, which is used in the manufacture of both flexible and rigid foams.

Trinitrotoluene (TNT). This explosive initially was the cause of toluene production from petroleum sources; however, it is now meeting more competition so little if any growth is expected.

Phenol. Dow uses toluene as a raw material at a 40 million pound/year phenol plant; little is known about the economics but observers consider the route to be commercially sound as Dow has now built two of these plants abroad. The market projections for toluene in 1970 are based on the assumption that Dow will double the capacity of its phenol-via-toluene plant. This seems plausible since Dow has additional phenol capacity of 230 million pounds/year based on benzene and chlorine.

Sulfates. Toluene is used to make toluene sulfonates; this detergent is expected to continue in its speciality role and show modest market growth.

INDIVIDUAL COMPANIES

Enjay and Shell are the two largest producers of toluene; each has a capacity of about 65 million gallons/year. Interestingly enough, these two companies also produce more benzene than any other U.S. companies. Chevron and Monsanto each has a capacity of 32 million gallons/year of toluene from reforming operation; additionally, Monsanto produces over 3 million gallons annually from its styrene monomer operations. No other company has a capacity of 30 million gallons/year although Amoco, Gulf, Mobil, Atlantic-Richfield, Sinclair, Sun, Texaco and Union Oil each have a capacity of 20 million gallons/year or more.

Enjay and Monsanto consume large quantities of toluene in dealkylation units to produce benzene; thus, Shell and Chevron sell more toluene than do Enjay and Monsanto.

Dow is by far the largest buyer of toluene; it consumes an estimated 50 million gallons/year in its dealkylation units; it makes 17 million gallons/year, although this is actually separated from a purchased benzene-toluene stream. Sunray DX buys 10 million gallons annually; Crown Central 5 million annually, and Suntide 4 million annually. These three companies consume the toluene in dealkylation units.

All other chemical and solvent buyers of toluene purchase less than 4 million gallons of toluene per year; however, American Oil does not use TEL in its premium gasoline and thus is a major purchaser of toluene.

There are a limited number of producers making large quantities of toluene; the two largest each make about 10 percent of U.S. requirements. On the other hand, there are a very large number of toluene consumers; thus good distribution systems and brokers play a major role in the selling of toluene.

HISTORICAL DATA

Table 5-4 presents data for past years and estimates for future years for selected statistics on toluene.

These data show a gradual increase in production of toluene in the United States. The increase is due to the toluene produced from petroleum sources as the toluene quantity produced by coke-oven operators and tar distillers has gradually declined. Refer to Figure 5-5.

TABLE 5-4—Historical Data—U.S. Production, Number of Producers, and Sales Value of Toluene

| Year | No. of Producers From Petroleum | PRODUCTION millions of gallons/year | | | Sales Millions of Gallons/ Year | Average Sales Price ¢/Gallon | Total Value of Production Millions of Dollars |
		Total	Tar Distillers and Coke-Oven Operators	Petroleum Operators			
1953	16	156	40	116	130	30	47
1954	16	159	36	123	126	29	46
1955	16	186	42	144	138	28	52
1956	16	174	43	131	135	26	45
1957	20	198	43	155	130	26	51
1958	23	239	32	207	137	21	50
1959	24	282	31	251	167	20	56
1960	24	274	33	241	200	19	57
1961	32	260	32	228	163	20	52
1962	34	361	30	331	207	19	59
1963	31	406	29	377	209	17	69
1964	31	498	28**	470	264**	17	85
1965*	31	554	27**	527	300**	17	94
1970*	..	750	27	723	400	16—18	120—135

Source: U.S. Tariff Commission.
  * Estimates.
  ** Includes an estimated 3 million gallons for tar distillates.

Average sales price has dropped gradually from 30¢/gallon in 1953 to the present figure of 17¢/gallon. Refer to Figure 5-6.

The combination of rising volume and falling price has resulted in a very slow rise in over-all value of toluene produced, although this has had its major rise

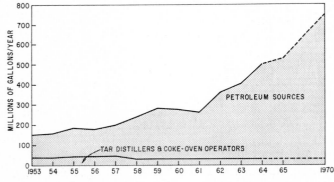

Figure 5-5. U.S. production of toluene, 1953 to 1970

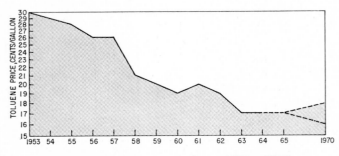

Figure 5-6. Sales price of toluene, 1953 to 1970

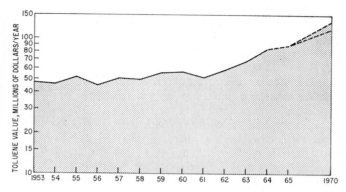

Figure 5-7. Value of U.S. toluene production, 1953 to 1970

in the last few years and reached $94 million in 1965 compared with $57 million in 1960. Refer to Figure 5-7.

Two other points are worth noting: (1) The number of producers of toluene from petroleum sources has approximately doubled over the past 10 years. (2) The amount of toluene consumed internally rose substantially after the installation of the HDA units in 1961; in 1964 the amount consumed internally exceeded the amount sold for the first time (this is shown in Table 5-4: 501 million produced, 230 sold, thus leaving 271 as internal consumption).

ECONOMICS

Toluene is produced as a coproduct, or byproduct, from one of the following operations: (1) Benzene, toluene, and xylenes are separated; (2) Only benzene and toluene are separated, and (3) Only toluene and xylenes are separated. In this latter operation benzene would not be made, as the C_6 stream would bypass the reformer.

The traditional method of costing toluene is to assign

all of the capital and operating costs for the reformer, solvent extraction unit, and separation equipment to the benzene and xylenes products. The toluene thus produced is valued only as a gasoline blending stock. This results in a benzene value considerably higher than a toluene value, although ironically, toluene has a higher blending value in a gasoline pool than does benzene.

This method of costing and pricing is a rational one when it is considered that more toluene is produced than is required in chemical, avgas, or solvent markets. The excess is dumped into the motor gasoline pool. Thus, the "alternate-use value" of toluene is its value to a refiner in a gasoline pool.

Toluene has a blending value in a gasoline pool of from 13¢ to 16¢/gallon; it is well to remember that no typical refinery exists, and accordingly there is a wide variation in octane requirements of various refineries depending on their crude oil, existing equipment and markets. Starting with a blending value of 13¢ to 16¢/gallon, then a refiner must sell the toluene for sufficient income to cover the distribution and sales costs in addition to a profit.

Distribution costs are an important element of over-all toluene costs. Much of the material produced on the Gulf Coast is consumed in the New England and Middle Atlantic states. The cost of handling the toluene and moving it to this area can add as much as 6¢/gallon to costs. Toluene has been selling in this large-market area for 19¢ to 23¢/gallon, depending on whether the price was at a major terminal or was a delivered price. Quantity of an individual purchase also makes a difference. Thus, a seller of toluene will net back something between 15 and 18¢/gallon at his plant. Big-volume, long-term contracts and large sales to the export market are believed to be in the lower part of this 15¢ to 18¢/gallon range.

While the value of toluene to a refiner's gasoline pool keeps the price from going too low, a high-side limit is established by the price a company is willing to pay for toluene to use as feed to a dealkylation unit. Since approximately a 10¢ differential between toluene and benzene is required to justify the erection of a dealkylation unit, then the benzene price serves to establish a ceiling on toluene price. With benzene in the 25¢ to 28¢/gallon range, then the upper limit established for toluene would be 15¢ to 18¢/gallon. Toluene must compete for the benzene market against the installation of reforming, extraction, and separation facilities in those refinery streams from which benzene is not being produced at present. At the 25¢ to 28¢/gallon benzene level, benzene production from these "marginal sources" of refinery benzene begins to look attractive.

THE FUTURE

The consumption of toluene will continue its slow but upward climb. Its many end-uses will keep the year-to-year swings relatively small. Its sales value will continue to be related to gasoline blending value, because there are some 3 to 3½ billion gallons of toluene produced annually in refinery reformers and only about ½ billion gallons of this is required for uses other than motor gasoline.

Toluene must continue to sell for slightly more than its blending value plus any extra costs incurred in handling, distribution, and sales efforts.

There are two main areas of uncertainty in future projections of toluene production and price:

1. *The raw material to be used in the manufacture of the benzene required in the future in the U.S.* Unless benzene is imported in large quantities into the U.S. from Puerto Rico or Europe, or unless the U.S. Government allows the production of benzene from low-cost foreign naphtha in Foreign-Trade Zones, then it appears likely that a considerable portion of future benzene requirements in the U.S. will be met by the dealkylation of toluene. In this case the price of toluene would tend to firm, especially since the growth of benzene-via-toluene not only consumes toluene but also results in less toluene being produced per gallon of benzene on an over-all basis.

2. *The price level of the U.S. gasoline market.* The average price realized by refiners for gasoline has shown a gradual decrease over the last few years. If this trend continues, it will tend to lessen the value of toluene in a refiner's gasoline pool. This value is affected not only by octane-levels and quantity requirements, but is also affected by the new refinery processes that will be available in the future to meet these octane and quantity requirements. Of course, underpinning the entire price structure of the refining industry is the price of U.S. crude oil; however, for political and other reasons, it is doubtful that this will change drastically in the next five years.

As each of the two areas of uncertainty represents a potentially-small change in toluene value, it is reasonable to conclude that toluene prices in the future should vary between 16¢ and 18¢/gallon level, compared with 17¢ in 1965.

This price range together with an estimated 750 million gallon production of toluene will result in the value of toluene produced in 1970 of $120 to $135 million dollars, versus $90 million in 1965.

If substantial quantities of toluene are consumed to make benzene, then an increasingly larger portion of toluene will be used internally rather than sold.

Literature Cited

1. Chemical companies manufacturing petrochemicals have been given limited access to imported petroleum feedstocks in

1966. This benefit amounts to about 5 percent of the manufacturing costs (including raw materials) of ethylene. Most industry observers expect that substantial additional changes will be made in this system in the future. See Reference 3, Chapter 1 for literature citations.

2. Tariff commission preliminary reports show 1965 production as 554 million pounds. Table 5-4 has been revised for 1965.

3. These companies have added or are adding additional capacity as of mid-1966.

4. See Reference 3, Chapter 1 for literature citations.

6

Naphthalene

UNTIL THE INTRODUCTION in 1961 of naphthalene obtained from petroleum, all of the nation's naphthalene came from coal-tar. However, since 1963 petroleum sources have provided slightly over 40 percent of the U.S. naphthalene and this figure is not expected to change much in the future. Phthalic anhydride accounts for 75 percent of all naphthalene consumed in the United States and is expected to continue in this dominant market role.

Because of the severe competition being faced by naphthalene against ortho-xylene as a feedstock for phthalic anhydride, the price of both coal-tar naphthalene and petroleum naphthalene are expected to weaken further (petroleum naphthalene is sold at a premium over coal-tar naphthalene because the higher purity of the petroleum naphthalene results in better yields in a phthalic plant). It is not expected that additional petroleum-naphthalene plants will be built, and, in fact, some of the ones already installed may be placed in other service. Because of these factors, naphthalene consumption in the United States is expected to grow only 3 percent a year, compared with 7 percent for phthalic anhydride. The value of output of naphthalene in 1965 in the United States was approximately $28 million, and it will not exceed this amount substantially in 1970 although output in terms of pounds will be up by 20 percent. About the only factor that could change this relatively unfavorable outlook for naphthalene would be for ortho-xylene to increase sharply in price, and this is not expected to happen.

MANUFACTURE

Naphthalene is obtained from two main sources:

Petroleum	42%
Tar distillers & coke ovens	58%
	100%

Since the installation of the petroleum-naphthalene plants in the early 1960's, these relative percentages have not changed substantially.

Naphthalene from Tar Distillers and Coke Ovens.
Crude coal tar is recovered in the byproduct coking of coal; this coal tar is then distilled into various fractions. The middle oil fraction, in which naphthalene is found, is the largest oil fraction in terms of volume. As a result, the amount of naphthalene present in coal tar is about 10 percent, which is substantially greater than the amount of any other chemical present.

The middle-oil fraction is processed by crystallizing, centrifuging, and washing to produce a crude naphthalene satisfactory for phthalic anhydride manufacture; these crude grades solidify at 74° to 78° C. Refined naphthalene is made from crude naphthalene by distillation and treatment first with hot caustic soda and then with concentrated sulfuric acid followed by sublimation or redistillation. This refined naphthalene melts above 79° C and is suitable for use in beta-naphthol, moth balls, surface-active agents and insecticides.

Naphthalene from Petroleum Refiners. There are five plants, owned by six companies as one is a joint venture, presently installed to make petro-naphthalene. These five plants use four different processes, as shown in Table 6-1. Additionally, there are several other processes available that have not yet been installed commercially.

All petro-naphthalene processes used commercially have the following items in common:

1. They produce a refined grade of naphthalene, having a melting point above 80° C.

2. They can operate on the higher boiling materials from a reformer, or a catalytic cracker gas oil, or by-products from steam cracking operations in which olefins are made. The chemistry of naphthalene production is shown in Figure 6-1.

TABLE 6-1—U.S. Producers of Naphthalene From Petroleum

COMPANY	LOCATION	PROCESS	CAPACITY millions of pounds/year
Ashland...........	Catlettsburg, Ky.	Ashland-UOP	120**
Cities Service......	East Chicago, Ill.	Union Oil	50***
Collier Carbon-Tidewater.......	Delaware City, Del.	Union Oil	100
Monsanto.........	Alvin, Tex.	Monsanto	85
Sun Oil...........	Toledo, Ohio	Sun Oil	100
Subtotal: From petroleum.......................			455
Subtotal: From tar distillers & coke ovens.........			550*
Grand Total: U.S. capacity from all sources....			1,005

* It is believed that this could be increased by 100 million pounds if warranted by demand at a profitable price.
** Industry rumors indicated that this unit was converted to cyclohexane manufacture but this is not believed to be the case.
*** Rumored to have shutdown.

TYPICAL REACTIONS

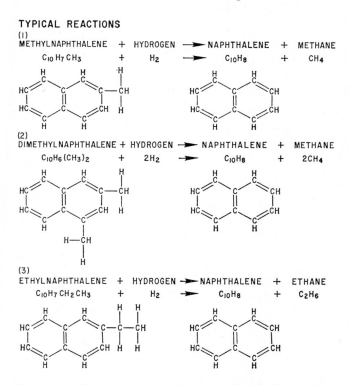

(1)

METHYLNAPHTHALENE + HYDROGEN ⟶ NAPHTHALENE + METHANE

$C_{10}H_7CH_3$ + H_2 ⟶ $C_{10}H_8$ + CH_4

(2)

DIMETHYLNAPHTHALENE + HYDROGEN ⟶ NAPHTHALENE + METHANE

$C_{10}H_6(CH_3)_2$ + $2H_2$ ⟶ $C_{10}H_8$ + $2CH_4$

(3)

ETHYLNAPHTHALENE + HYDROGEN ⟶ NAPHTHALENE + ETHANE

$C_{10}H_7CH_2CH_3$ + H_2 ⟶ $C_{10}H_8$ + C_2H_6

Figure 6-1. Chemistry of naphthalene production from refinery streams

Two of the four processes definitely use catalysts, while details on this point have not been clearly indicated for the other two processes.

The first petro-naphthalene plant to be operated commercially is the one owned by Ashland; it uses a process developed jointly by Ashland and UOP. The flow dia-

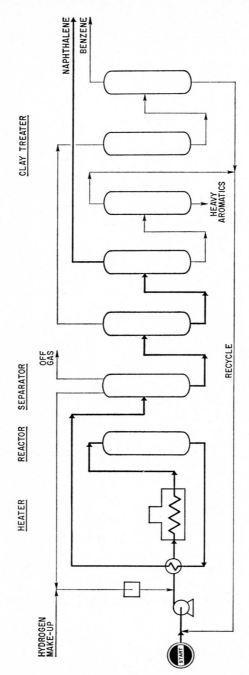

Figure 6-2. Ashland-U.O.P. method for naphthalene manufacture[1]

gram for this process is shown in Figure 6-2. The process has three basic steps: (1) Hydrogen and the alkylnaphthalene feed are combined and then heated in a furnace to reaction temperature; (2) The reaction takes place in a catalytic reactor, and (3) The reactor effluent is separated in a series of four columns. This unit can also be used to produce benzene from toluene, and there are many installations of this process in this service.

The only petro-naphthalene process to be used in two commercial installations is the one developed by Union Oil and used by Cities Service and a Collier Carbon-Tidewater Oil joint venture (Collier Carbon is a subsidiary of Union Oil). This process is shown in Figure 6-3. It follows the basic three steps of the Ash-

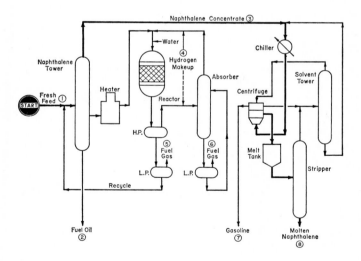

Figure 6-3. Union Oil's naphthalene manufacturing process

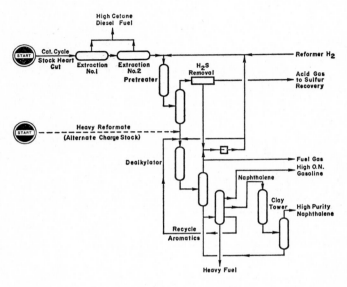

Figure 6-4. Sun Oil uses this type of naphthalene manufacturing process

land-UOP process; however, it uses a different purification system. It uses a catalytic reactor.

A third process is the one developed and installed by Sun. This is believed to use a thermal dealkylation rather than a catalytic one. This process is shown in Figure 6-4. It uses the same basic steps as the other processes, although a different purification system is used. This diagram shows a feed-preparation section; in actual fact, it may be desirable to use a feed-preparation section with the other processes. The need for this section depends on the stocks available in a given refinery and the markets available for the refinery products. However, generally a feed below 70 percent in aromatics content will require feed treatment to increase the aromatics

content; these extra facilities usually cannot be justified if the aromatics content is above 95 percent. Special study is required when it is between 70 percent
and 95 percent.

The fourth process which has been installed commercially was developed by Monsanto and used in a
plant that went onstream in 1962.

TABLE 6-2—U.S. Markets for Naphthalene, 1965 and 1970

	Millions of pounds 1965	1970
Phthalic anhydride........................	610	660
Insecticides.................................	100	150
Beta-naphthol and moth balls............	90	120
Miscellaneous.............................	20	30
Grand Total...........................	820[4]	960

MARKETS

About 75 percent of U.S. naphthalene is consumed
as a raw material in the production of phthalic anhydride, so any analysis of naphthalene markets must include a review of phthalic anhydride. A complicating
factor is that either petro-naphthalene, coal-tar naphthalene, or ortho-xylene can be used as a raw material
for phthalic anhydride; accordingly, any projections of
future naphthalene consumption are dependent on the
outcome of this contest for the phthalic market.

With this background in mind, it appears that naphthalene consumption in the United States will grow
at an annual rate of about 3 percent a year; thus,
1970 consumption will be 960 million pounds, compared with 820 million pounds[4] in 1965. Refer to Table
6-2 and Figure 6-5.

Let's now discuss the two largest markets.

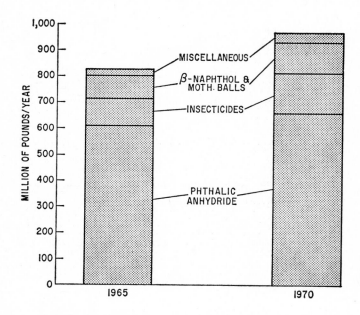

Figure 6-5. U.S. naphthalene consumption follows this pattern, 1965 and 1970

Phthalic Anhydride. Phthalic anhydride production in the United States is expected to grow at an annual rate of 7 percent, thus resulting in a 1970 figure of 820 million pounds versus 580 million pounds[5] in 1965. Vinyl plasticizers represent the largest market, followed by alkyd resins and polyester resins; refer to Figure 6-6.

Vinyl Plasticizers. This market accounts for 40 percent of phthalic anhydride consumption now and is growing rapidly because of the increased demand for higher quality and more specialized plastics, both of

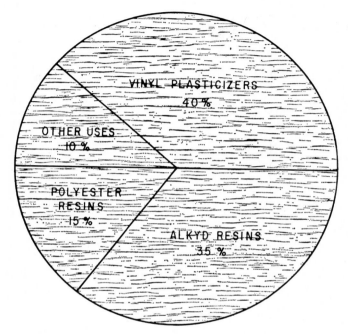

Figure 6-6. Uses of phthalic anhydride are distributed like this is the U.S. during 1965

which increase plasticizer use. By 1970 this outlet will account for 45 percent of phthalic consumption.

Alkyd Resins. These were once the largest outlet for phthalic anhydride, but alkyd coatings have been losing a portion of the market to other surface coatings. Since the entire field is growing, alkyd resins should be able to maintain its present consumption level of phthalic anhydride. This will result in a market share of 25 percent of phthalic in 1970 versus 35 percent in 1965.

TABLE 6-3—U.S. Producers of Phthalic Anhydride

Company	Location	Raw Material**	Cap. millions of lbs/yr	Est. Consumption of naphthalene —1965 millions of lbs/yr
Allied[6].......	Chicago, Ill.	coal-tar naphthalene	35*	0
	El Segundo Calif.	ortho-xylene	25	—
	Frankford, Pa.	coal-tar naphthalene	80	88
	Ironton, Ohio	coal-tar naphthalene	35	39
Chevron[6]	Perth Amboy, N.J.	ortho-xylene	30	—
	Richmond, Calif.	ortho-xylene	20*	—
Grace[6]	Fords, N.J.	coal-tar naphthalene†	25	28
		petro-naphthalene	25	28
Koppers[6]	Bridgeport, Pa.	coal-tar naphthalene†	50	55
Monsanto	Bridgeport, N.J.	petro-naphthalene	50	55
	St. Louis, Mo.	coal-tar naphthalene‡	70	77
Pittsburgh Chem.	Neville Is., Pa.	coal-tar naphthalene	50	55
Reichhold	Azusa, Calif.	coal-tar naphthalene†	8	9
	Elizabeth, N.J.	petro-naphthalene	30	33
Sherwin-Williams	Chicago, Ill.	petro-naphthalene	20	22
Stepan[6]	Millsdale, Ill.	ortho-xylene or petro-naphthalene	40	—
Tenneco	Fords, N.J.	ortho-xylene	12	—
Thompson[6]	Hebronville, Mass.	coal-tar naphthalene	10	11
Union Carbide[6]	Institute, W. Va.	petro-naphthalene	50	55
Witco	Chicago, Ill.	coal-tar naphthalene	20	22
	Perth Amboy, N.J.	coal-tar naphthalene†	30	33
TOTAL—U.S. PHTHALIC ANHYDRIDE CAPACITY			715	610[4]

* It is believed that this plant is idle.
† This plant can also operate on ortho-xylene.
‡ Reports indicate this plant may be operating on ortho-xylene.
** Petro-naphthalene can be used in those plants shown with coal-tar naphthalene, and purified coal-tar naphthalene can be used in petro-naphthalene plants.

Polyester Resins. This is a rapidly growing market and should consume 20 percent of the U.S. phthalic in 1970, compared with 15 percent in 1965. Polyesters are being used in boats, automobile bodies, trailers and trucks.

Miscellaneous. This use includes dyes, pharmaceuticals, dielectric materials, and decorative laminates. These outlets will continue to consume about 10 percent of the U.S. phthalic anhydride.

U.S. producers of phthalic anhydride are listed in Table 6-3; an indication of their naphthalene consumption in 1965 is also given.

Insecticides. This outlet for naphthalene has been growing rapidly and is expected to continue this growth at an annual rate of 8 percent. This will result in a 1970 consumption of naphthalene of 150 million pounds versus 100 in 1965.[4] Accurate figures are not available in this area of naphthalene consumption and these numbers should be considered as rough approximations.

INDIVIDUAL COMPANIES

Table 6-4 lists the major sellers and buyers of naphthalene in the United States.

Monsanto, Allied, and Union Carbide are the largest consumers of naphthalene, with each consuming more than 100 million pounds annually. However, as both Allied and Monsanto are major manufacturers of naphthalene, Union Carbide purchases the largest quantities of naphthalene.

No other company approaches Union Carbide in over-all size of purchases. Grace, Pittsburgh Chemical, and Reichhold are the next largest buyers, with annual purchases running 40 to 60 million pounds. The quantities bought by Monsanto and Allied are not known, but their purchases could also be in this range.

The three major sellers are Ashland, Collier Carbon-Tidewater and Sun Oil; their combined sales approximate 260 million pounds annually.

TABLE 6-4——Major Sellers and Buyers of U.S. Naphthalene, 1965

Company	Naphthalene Quantity in millions of pounds/year			
	Use	Make	Sell	Buy
Ashland....................	0	100	100	—
Collier Carbon-Tidewater...	0	80	80	—
Sun Oil....................	0	80	80	—
Consumers for phthalic anhydride manufacture:				
Union Carbide..............	55*	0	—	55*
Grace.....................	56	0	—	56
Pittsburgh Chemical........	55	0	—	55
Monsanto..................	132**	80	—	52**
Reichhold.................	42	0	—	42
Sherwin-Williams..........	22	0	—	22
Thompson.................	11	0	—	11
Allied.....................	127	yes	?	?
Koppers...................	55	yes	?	?
Witco.....................	55	yes	?	?
Miscellaneous consumption for purposes other than phthalic anhydride manufacture...................	210*	yes	?	?
Totals..................	820⁴	800***	600	600

Notes:
   * Including the naphthalene it consumes in the manufacture of the insecticide, "Sevin," Union Carbide is believed to purchase and consume more than 100 million pounds/year.
   ** Unconfirmed reports indicate part of this consumption may be ortho-xylene instead of naphthalene.
   *** Imports equal 20 million pounds.
   **** In addition to the Allied, Koppers, and Witco listed above, the following companies also make naphthalene from coal-tar: Coopers Creek Chemical Corp., Neville Chemical Co., Pennsylvania Industrial Chemical Corp., Productol Co., Reilly Tar and Chemical Corp., Ruberoid Co.

HISTORICAL DATA

Table 6-5 presents data for past years and estimates for future years for selected statistics relating to naphthalene.

These data show an early peak in naphthalene production and consumption in the 1955-1956 period. This period was followed by declines in these two statistics for a few years; however, every year since 1961, both have shown substantial gain and have passed the earlier peak.

TABLE 6-5—Historical Data—U.S. Production, Number of Producers, and Sales Value of Naphthalene

Year	NUMBER OF PRODUCERS		PRODUCTION millions of pounds/year			IMPORTS millions of pounds/year	APPARENT CONSUMPTION millions of pounds/year	SALES millions of pounds/year	AVERAGE SALES PRICE ¢/pound		TOTAL VALUE OF ALL PRODUCTION millions of dollars
	From petro-leum	From tar-distillers & coke-oven operators	Total	Tar distillers and coke-oven operators	Petroleum				Tar distillers & coke ovens	Petro-leum	
1953	0	11	276	276	0	83	359	200	5.5	—	15
1954	0	12	295	295	0	67	362	224	4.5	—	13
1955	0	12	477	477	0	122	599	339	5.8	—	28
1956	0	12	491	491	0	79	570	289	6.4	—	31
1957	0	13	420	420	0	93	513	276	6.3	—	26
1958	0	13	345	345	0	81	426	213	6.3	—	22
1959	0	13	425	425	0	59	484	267	4.8	—	20
1960	1	12	517	517	0	41	558	310	5.1	—	26
1961	4	11	497	447**	50**	102	599	299	6.0**	6.5**	30
1962	6	11	591	424	167	39	630	423	4.6	5.9	29
1963	6	9	627	339	288	28	655	442	3.4	5.1	26
1964	6	7	740	425	315	20	760	470	2.7	4.2	25
1965*	6		813	461	352	20	833	510	2.7	4.0	27
1970*	—	—	960	550	410	Nil	960	550	2.7	2.7–3.2	26–28

Source: U.S. Tariff Commission, Bureau of the Census.
* Estimates.
** Estimated by author; U.S. Tariff Commission gives one total for all sources.

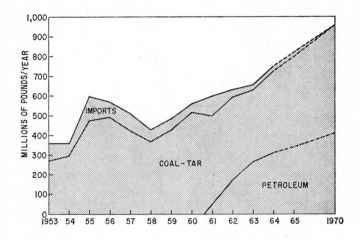

Figure 6-7. Naphthalene consumed in the U.S. came from these sources, 1953-1970

Imports provided 10 percent to 20 percent of the naphthalene consumed in the United States until 1963 at which time the percentage dropped to less than 5 percent; in 1965 the figure was less than 3 percent. Refer to Figure 6-7.

Average sales price varied widely, but was at the 6.0¢/pound level when petro-naphthalene was introduced in 1961. Under the impact of competition from ortho-xylene in the raw material market for phthalic anhydride, the price of both petro-naphthalene and coal-tar naphthalene dropped sharply to the 1965 figure of about 4.0¢/pound for petro-naphthalene and 3.2¢/pound for coal-tar naphthalene. (Petro-naphthalene sells at a premium over coal-tar naphthalene because it is a purer material that results in better plant yields.) Refer to Figure 6-8.

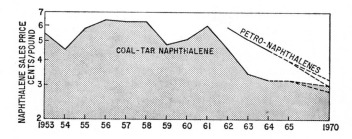

Figure 6-8. Sales prices of naphthalene followed this pattern in the U.S., 1953-1970

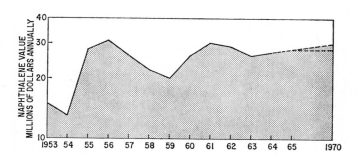

Figure 6-9. Value of U.S. naphthalene production, 1953-1970

The total value of all naphthalene produced in 1965 was about $28 million, or less than the all-time high of $31 million reached in 1956. Refer to Figure 6-9. However, production in 1965 was 67 percent higher than in 1956.

Note that external sales accounted for 60 to 75 percent of total production.

Another interesting point is that the number of producers of coal-tar naphthalene has gradually declined:

the number of producers of petro-naphthalene rose sharply initially but has now levelled off.

ECONOMICS

The economics of producing naphthalene from coal-tar vary widely depending on the operations of the individual company. These will not be discussed further.

The economics of producing naphthalene from petroleum will be discussed in detail. The evaluation is based on published data.[1]

As will be seen in the table below, the largest variable in determining the cost of the product is the unit value of the raw material. Because of the wide differences between various refineries this is particularly difficult to estimate on a generalized basis.

One reference states that methylnaphthalene fractions are worth 1½ to 2¢/pound;[2] it is presumed that this refers to a material, such as reformate bottoms, containing greater than 95 percent aromatics since aromatic cycle stocks from catalytic cracking units are generally valued at less than 1¢/pound in refineries.

Reformate bottoms could be obtained by increasing the endpoint (that is, increase the upper limit on the boiling range) of the naphtha normally charged to the reformer; in this case some additional gasoline is made and must be sold, while less middle distillate (kerosine, heating, or diesel oil) is available from the refinery. Therefore, the "cost" of this heavy reformate, containing virtually 100 percent aromatics, must include any gain or loss attributed to the changed output from the refinery. The evaluation in the table below is based on a charge stock containing 100 percent aromatics with a boiling range of 400° to 550° F. To show the effect of value of raw material a lower limit of 1.2¢/pound and an upper limit of 2.2¢/pound are used as the two extremes.

As mentioned in the section on manufacturing, an

aromatic cycle stock from a refinery catalytic cracking unit can be used; however, as it contains only about 40 to 70 percent aromatics, the aromatics and the non-aromatics portions must be separated before the cycle stock is suitable for feed to the naphthalene unit. Preliminary estimates of costs of raw materials indicate that the resulting cost of a specially-prepared catalytic cycle oil will be comparable to that of reformate bottoms.[2]

A third possible source of raw material is the by-product material boiling in the 400°-550° F produced by steam cracking in the manufacture of light olefins. The economics of using this material are believed to be comparable with those of the first two materials.

With this background concerning raw material costs, the detailed costs involved in making naphthalene will now be examined:

Basis: 75 million pounds/year of naphthalene
U.S. Gulf Coast location

Battery limits capital	= $2.85 million or 3.8¢/annual pound
Offsite capital at 33% of B.L.	= $950,000
Total capital	= $3.8 million or 5.1¢/annual pound
Direct operating costs	= 0.7¢/pound
Return on investment	= 20% before tax
Sales and administrative overhead	= 0.3¢/pound

All figures in cents/pound

Value of raw material	1.2	2.2
Cost of raw material	3.5	6.4
Hydrogen, at fuel value	0.1	0.1
Benzene credit, at 25¢/gal. of Bz.	(1.5)	(1.5)
Heavy product credit, at 0.8¢/pound	(0.1)	(0.1)
Offgas credit, at 20¢/million Btu	(0.6)	(0.6)
Net cost of raw material	1.4	4.3

Direct operating costs	0.7	0.7
Subtotal: Out of pocket costs	2.1	5.0
Depreciation, at 10% of B.L. plant	0.4	0.4
Subtotal: Breakeven costs	2.5	5.4
Return on investment, at 20%	1.0	1.0
Subtotal without sales & admin.	3.5	6.4
Sales & Admin. Overhead	0.3	0.3
Grand Total	3.8	6.7

These results are plotted in Figure 6-10. From this figure it can be seen that with naphthalene sales value of 4¢/pound, a refiner must value his raw material at less than 1.8¢ to 1.9¢/pound to cover "out-of-pocket" costs and 1.2¢ to 1.3¢/pound to earn 20 percent before taxes on his investment.

These figures seem to indicate that a refiner making naphthalene at the current price level of about 4¢ is covering his out-of-pocket costs but certainly is not earning a satisfactory return on his investment. Thus he will continue to operate the unit unless he can find a more profitable use for it.

There are two other factors which make the profit picture for a refiner a little brighter:

1. With today's knowledge, a plant to produce 75 million pounds of naphthalene could probably be built for less than the capital indicated above. One indication of this is that Ashland incrementally expanded its unit from the 75 million pound/year level to one of 120 million pounds/year. It is believed this expansion was done at a small fraction of the cost of comparable capacity obtained from a new plant. This reduction in cost of capital would have little effect on the out-of-pocket costs but would lower the sales price required to earn a satisfactory investment.

2. The use of an aromatic raw material to make naphthalene has the net result of reducing the amount

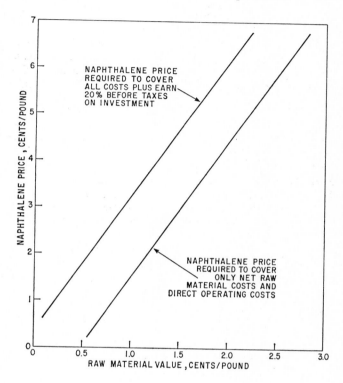

Figure 6-10. Naphthalene price to give various financial return on plant investment

of aromatics in a refiner's products in the 400°-550° F boiling range (middle distillates). This results in improving the quality of the middle distillate by increasing its smoke point and its Diesel Index. The dollar value this has to a refiner depends on his markets, crude oil and available processing equipment.

THE FUTURE

There is little doubt that naphthalene producers will face more severe competition in the future from ortho-xylene as an alternate feedstock to phthalic anhydride than in the past. There are several reasons for this:

1. Ortho-xylene has a higher theoretical yield as a raw material to phthalic than does naphthalene, as shown in Figure 6-11. (At 100 percent of theory, one pound of phthalic requires 0.72 pounds of ortho-xylene or 0.86 pounds of naphthalene.) Since ortho-xylene is a relatively new feedstock for phthalic production, it has not as yet benefited from a vast amount of plant operating experience as has naphthalene. Undoubtedly, plant technical service and research groups will develop processes that will produce more pounds of phthalic

(1)   ORTHO-XYLENE + OXYGEN ⟶ PHTHALIC ANHYDRIDE + WATER

$C_6H_4(CH_3)_2$ + $3O_2$ ⟶ $C_6H_4(CO)_2O$ + $3H_2O$

M. W. = 106   96   148   54

OR

THEORETICAL YIELDS = 0.72   0.65   I POUND   0.37

(2)   NAPHTHALENE + OXYGEN ⟶ PHTHALIC ANHYDRIDE + WATER + CARBON DIOXIDE

$C_{10}H_8$ + $4\text{-}1/2\,O_2$ ⟶ $C_6H_4(CO_2)_2O$ + $2H_2O$ + $2CO_2$

M. W. = 128   144   148   36   88

OR

THEORETICAL YIELDS = 0.86   0.97   I POUND   0.24   0.59

Figure 6-11. Chemistry of phthalic anhydride manufacture from naphthalene and ortho-xylene

anhydride per pound of ortho-xylene than from naphthalene. Present processes use about one pound of either ortho-xylene or petro-naphthalene per pound of phthalic.

2. Many of the old phthalic anhydride plants are unable to use ortho-xylene as a raw material without extensive modifications and therefore the owners have been unable to exert maximum economic pressure on the naphthalene sellers. A number of these old plants have a relatively small capacity and thus tend to be uneconomic from this standpoint also; thus they will eventually be replaced with newer plants designed to use ortho-xylene as a raw material. In fact some of the newer plants will be designed to use either ortho-xylene or naphthalene as a feedstock.

3. Some of the petroleum-naphthalene plants were installed on the basis of a fixed-price contract for the product; while these prices have been lowered substantially as the phthalic producers were put under pressure because of phthalic price drops (from 18¢/ pound in 1960 to 8½¢ in 1965), the phthalic producers were still not in a position to exert maximum economic pressure. When these contracts expire, this pressure will be exerted.

4. Ortho-xylene has been selling in the 3 to 3¼¢/ pound range and is expected to continue in this general range for some time.

Because of these items, it seems that petro-naphthalene will eventually have to sell in the same range as ortho-xylene, while coal-tar naphthalene will have to sell at a slightly lower level. This is based on the assumption that naphthalene continues to be consumed in the phthalic market; which, of course, presently accounts for 75 percent of present consumption of naphthalene.

Thus a price of 3¢ or slightly less can be expected for

coal-tar naphthalene and a price of about 3¢ can be expected for petro-naphthalene sometime in the next few years. At these prices it will not be profitable for a refiner to install a new naphthalene unit; in fact, a refiner will be searching for ways to convert his existing naphthalene unit to other uses, such as benzene or cyclohexane manufacture. As shown in Figure 6-10, a refiner will cover his out-of-pocket costs and net 1.5¢/pound for his raw material; hence he will probably not shut down the unit entirely. However, it must be remembered that this raw material value is for one that contains 95-100 percent aromatics and is suitable for feed to the unit without further treatment.

Under the conditions mentioned above, plus assuming some petro-naphthalene units are switched to other service while others are "debottlenecked" with very little capital, it seems reasonable to assume that about 410 million pounds of petro-naphthalene and 550 million pounds of coal-tar naphthalene will be produced in the United States in 1970.[4] Their average sales prices are expected to be 2.8 to 3.0¢/pound for coal-tar naphthalene and 3.0 to 3.2¢/pound for petro-naphthalene. Consequently, the total value of naphthalene produced in the United States in 1970 is expected to be $28 to $30 million dollars annually, or about the same dollar value as in 1965 (refer to Figure 6-9).

It appears that the only factor that could change this picture radically would be for the price of ortho-xylene to rise sharply, and this is not expected to happen.

Literature Cited

1. Asselin, G. F. and R. A. Erickson, "Benzene and Naphthalene from Petroleum by the Hydeal Process," *Chemical Engineering Progress,* 58:47-52, April 1962.

2. "Hydrodealkylation Processes," *Industrial and Engineering Chemistry,* 54: 28-33, February 1962.

3. See Reference 3, Chapter 1 for literature citations.

4. Tariff Commission preliminary reports show 1965 production as 813 million pounds; however, because of conversion of naphthalene from one grade to another, all Tariff Commission production figures may be overstated by as much as 10-20%. Thus, a more realistic estimate of naphthalene markets should show reductions in naphthalene consumption in most areas, especially "Insecticides" and "beta-naphthol and moth balls." See *Oil, Paint and Drug Reporter* March 14, 1966, page 3.

5. Tariff Commission preliminary reports show 1965 production as 579 million pounds. However, because production of Stepan chemical had not been included in these reports until early 1966; the production figures are understated, by about 35 million pounds in 1965.

6. These companies have added or are adding additional capacity as of mid-1966.

7

Xylenes

APPROXIMATELY 98 percent of the xylenes separated in the United States come from petroleum sources and this will continue to be the case in the future. Mixed xylenes are separated from refinery reformate streams and are used as a source of the individual xylene isomers, as a solvent, and as a gasoline blending stock. Mixed xylenes are also a source of ethylbenzene, which is found in mixed xylene streams because its boiling point is so close to those of the xylene isomers. The mixed xylenes separated represent only about 10 percent of the total available in U.S. refineries; the remainder is used in gasoline without having been separated.

Output of mixed xylenes depends on the production of other aromatics, such as toluene, and on the requirements for the individual isomers; this output of separated mixed xylenes is expected to increase at an annual rate of about 4 percent and will reach 490 million gallons in 1970 versus 395 million in 1965. There is expected to be little change in price.

Ortho-xylene is used primarily as a feedstock for phthalic anhydride, both in the U.S. and abroad. Over-all U.S. output will increase at the rate of 4 percent annually until 1970, at which time U.S. production will approximate 410 million pounds versus 330 in 1965. U.S. consumption will grow at a substantially higher rate but will be partially offset by a drop in export sales; export sales accounted for 70 percent of U.S. ortho-xylene production in 1965. The price of ortho-xylene is related to its gasoline-blending value and is expected to change little in the next five years.

Para-xylene is used in the manufacture of raw materials for polyester fibers; as it is the primary raw material for both dimethyl terephthalate (DMT) and terephthalic acid (TPA) its production will increase regardless of whether DMT or TPA becomes the main raw material for polyesters. A growth rate in U.S. production of 24 percent annually is forecast between 1965 and 1970; the resulting production in 1970 will be 1,200 million pounds versus 405 million in 1965. Past studies by the author indicate that such a substantial increase in production rate will bring substantially lower prices; based on these studies it seems reasonable to expect a para-xylene price in the 5.0¢/pound region by 1970, compared with about 8.0¢ in 1965. Present economic studies indicate a lower level for para-xylene price to be about 7½¢/pound. If para-xylene output increases as expected and if the price in 1970 is between 5.0 and 7½¢/pound, then the value of 1970 output will be $60 to $90 million compared with $31 million in 1965.

MANUFACTURE

Mixed xylenes are obtained from two main sources:

Petroleum	98 percent
Coaltar and cokeoven light oils	2 percent
	100 percent

The percentage of xylenes obtained from coal is gradually decreasing. Manufacture from this source will not be discussed.

There are three xylene isomers—ortho, meta, and para. The ortho and para isomers are separated from the mixed xylene stream for use as a chemical intermediate. Essentially all of the ortho and para that are so separated are obtained from mixed xylenes produced by the petroleum industry.

NAME	STRUCTURE	FORMULA	SIMPLIFIED FORMULA	MOLECULAR WEIGHT	BOILING POINT, °F.	MELTING POINT, °F.
ORTHO-XYLENE	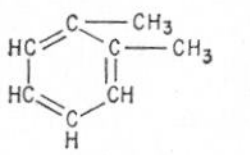	$1,2-C_6H_4(CH_3)_2$	C_8H_{10}	106.2	292.0	-13.3
META-XYLENE	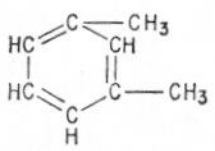	$1,3-C_6H_4(CH_3)_2$	C_8H_{10}	106.2	282.4	-54.2
PARA-XYLENE	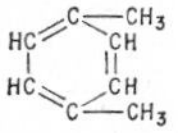	$1,4-C_6H_4(CH_3)_2$	C_8H_{10}	106.2	281.0	+55.9
ETHYLBENZENE	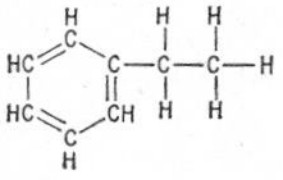	$C_6H_5C_2H_5$	C_8H_{10}	106.2	277.1	-138.9

Figure 7-1. Formulas and physical constants for the xylenes and ethylbenzene[8]

Ethylbenzene has the same molecular weight—106.2 —and the same formula—C_8H_{10}—as the three xylene isomers; its boiling point is a few degrees less than the lowest boiling xylene isomer (para). The formulas and constants for the xylenes and ethylbenzene are shown in Figure 7-1.

The manufacture of mixed xylenes, the individual xylene isomers, and ethylbenzene are related and so will be discussed together.

Xylenes and ethylbenzene are formed when naphthenes are reformed in a refinery reformer to produce aromatics.

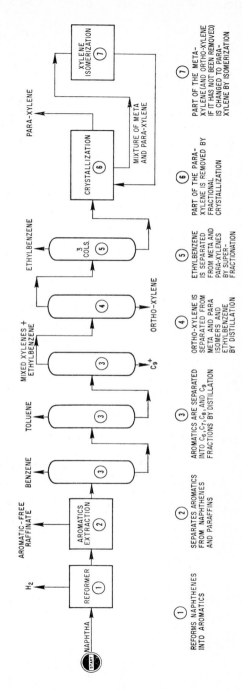

Figure 7-2. Scheme for the manufacture of aromatics including ortho- and para-xylene from naphtha. Note: This is a typical processing scheme; various combinations of the following are being practiced commercially: 1) The C₆'s are not reformed so benzene is not produced; in this case, the first column in Step No. 3 is omitted, 2) The ethylbenzene is not separated so Step No. 5 is omitted, 3) The ortho-xylene is not separated so Step No. 4 is omitted, 4) Ethylbenzene is removed before the ortho-xylene so Steps No. 4 and 5 are reversed, 5) The para-xylene is not separated so Steps No. 6 and 7 are omitted.

Figure 7-2 shows a typical processing scheme starting with the reformer as the first step. The chemistry of xylene and ethylbenzene formation in the reformer is shown in Figure 7-3.

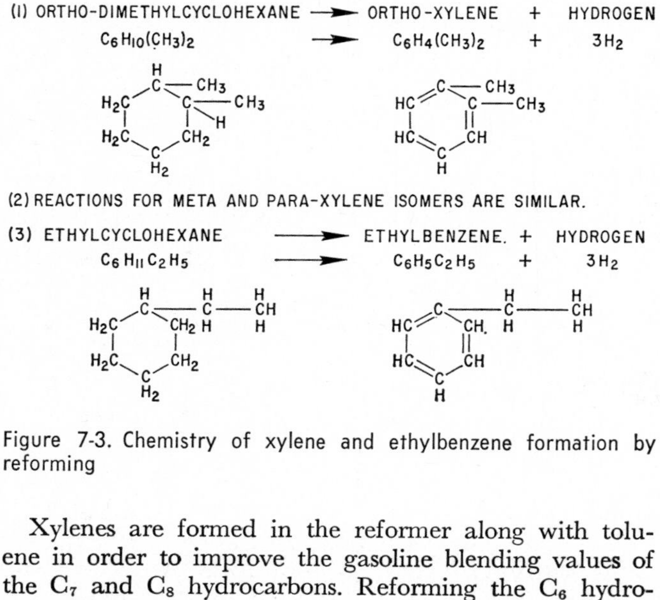

(1) ORTHO-DIMETHYLCYCLOHEXANE $\longrightarrow$ ORTHO-XYLENE + HYDROGEN

$C_6H_{10}(CH_3)_2$ $\longrightarrow$ $C_6H_4(CH_3)_2$ + $3H_2$

(2) REACTIONS FOR META AND PARA-XYLENE ISOMERS ARE SIMILAR.

(3) ETHYLCYCLOHEXANE $\longrightarrow$ ETHYLBENZENE. + HYDROGEN

$C_6H_{11}C_2H_5$ $\longrightarrow$ $C_6H_5C_2H_5$ + $3H_2$

Figure 7-3. Chemistry of xylene and ethylbenzene formation by reforming

Xylenes are formed in the reformer along with toluene in order to improve the gasoline blending values of the C_7 and C_8 hydrocarbons. Reforming the C_6 hydrocarbons is usually only carried out if the benzene is to be extracted, since reforming C_6's only for octane improvement cannot usually be justified.

If aromatics are to be recovered then the next step is the separation of the aromatics from the paraffins and residual naphthenes. In this process the aromatics are dissolved in a solvent such as diethylene glycol or sulfolane and then stripped from the solvent (refer to Figure 7-4 for flow diagram showing a unit using diethylene glycol).

The third step is the separation of the various aromatic fractions by distillation. The distillation train used is a function of the particular aromatics to be recovered. The one shown in Figure 7-2 is used when each of the separate aromatic fractions is to be recovered.

Most companies in the benzene and toluene business stop at this point. However, those separating ethylbenzene or one or more of the xylene isomers use one or more of the next four steps.

The fourth step is the separation of the ortho-xylene by distillation. Ortho-xylene boils 9.6° F higher than the closest boiling other isomer, meta.

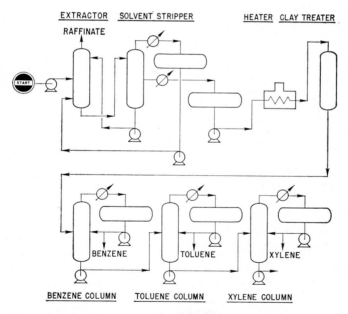

Figure 7-4. Aromatics can be separated from paraffins using this diethylene glycol extraction scheme

TABLE 7-1—U.S. Xylene Producers from Petroleum Feedstock

Company	Location	Other Aromatics Produced				Xylene Capacity		
		Benzene	Toluene	Ethylbenzene	Naphthalenes	Millions of Gallons/Year Mixed*	Millions of Pounds/Year Ortho-	Para-
Amoco	Texas City, Tex.	X	X	..	..	30	...	...
Ashland	N. Tonawanda, N.Y.	X	X	..	..	20	...	...
	Catlettsburg, Ky.	X	X	..	X	28	...	...
Chevron	El Segundo, Calif.	X	X	..	..	50	30	90
	Richmond, Calif.	X	X	..	..	20	100	110
Cities Service	Lake Charles, La.	..	..	..	..	72	120	X[10]
Cosden	Big Spring, Tex.	X	X	X	..	18	12	6
Crown Central	Houston, Tex.	X	X	..	..	10	20	...
Enjay	Baton Rouge, La.	X	X	..	..	40	...	X[10]
	Baytown, Tex.	X	X	X	..	50	175***	150
Hess	Corpus Christi, Tex.	X	X	..	..	30	75	...
Leonard	Mount Pleasant, Mich.	X	X	..	..	6	...	...
Marathon	Detroit, Mich.	**	**	..	..	14	...	...
	Texas City, Tex.	X	X	..	..	12	...	...
Mobil	Beaumont, Tex.	X	X	..	..	40	...	...
Monsanto	Alvin, Tex.	X	X	X	X	40	...	...
Pontiac	Corpus Christi, Tex.	X	X	..	..	18	10	...
Shell	Houston, Tex.	X	X	..	..	62	...	X[10]
	Odessa, Tex.	X	X	..	..	10	...	...
	Wilmington, Calif.	X	X	..	..	30	...	...
	Wood River, Ill.	X	X	..	..	60	...	...
Signal	Houston, Tex.	X	X	X	..	20	...	15
Sinclair	Houston, Tex.	X[10]	X	****	..	45	75	115
	Marcus Hook, Pa.	..	X	..	..	30	...	15
Sun	Marcus Hook, Pa.	X	X	..	..	30	...	...
Sunray DX	Tulsa, Okla.	X	X	..	..	22	...	...
Suntide	Corpus Christi, Tex.	X	X	X	..	20	32	65*****
Tenneco	Chalmette, La.	X	X	X	..	30	22	...
Union Oil-Atlantic	Nederland, Tex.	X	X	..	..	36	...	...
Union Oil	Lemont, Ill.	X	X	..	..	44	...	...
Vickers	Potwin, Kans.	X	X	..	..	6	...	...
Total from petroleum feedstocks						943	671	566
Total from coal-tar						10	...	...
Grand Total, U.S.						953	...	...
Capacity to be added later in 1966 and 1967								
Amoco	Texas City, Tex.	..	..	..	..	...	...	200
Chevron	Pascagoula, Miss.	..	..	..	..	...	...	300
Coastal States	Corpus Christi, Tex.	X	X	..	..	12	...	X[10]
Shell	Deer Park, Tex.	..	..	..	..	...	...	100
Southwestern	Corpus Christi, Tex.	X	X	..	..	12	...	...
Suntide	Corpus Christi, Tex.	..	..	..	..	...	...	60
Total to be added in 1966/1967						24	...	660
Grand Total, all U.S. capacity end of 1967						977	...	1226

Notes: *These are estimates of approximate capacities based on the plant's benzene and/or other aromatics capacity. However, in many of the above cases the mixed xylenes are not separated from some of the other aromatics, as less than 50 percent of the total capacity shown here is recovered as mixed xylenes.
** Sells a mixed benzene-toluene stream to Dow.
*** It is believed that part of the equipment previously used for ortho-xylene separation has been removed from this service; thus this capacity is not operating.
**** Ethylbenzene is separated by Sinclair-Koppers joint venture.
***** Fifty of the 65 million pounds at Suntide, Corpus Christi, are a joint venture with Amoco

In step number five, the ethylbenzene is separated in a series of three columns; these columns in effect do the separation of one very tall column but three columns are used because one column would be too tall. Ethylbenzene boils only 3.9° F below para-xylene, the lowest boiling of the xylene isomers; thus a tall column with high reflux ratio is needed.

Also it should be remembered that the separation of the ethylbenzene and ortho-xylene makes the separation of para-xylene easier.

Para-xylene boils only 1.4° F below meta-xylene; accordingly, separation by distillation would be too expensive. Fortunately, the melting point of para-xylene is 55.9° F, or about 100° F higher than that of meta-xylene and 69.2° F higher than the melting point of the

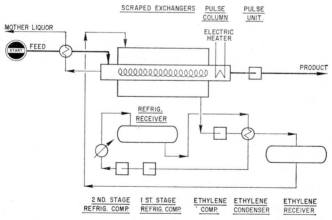

Figure 7-5. Crystallization process for the separation of para-xylene[1]

closest isomer, ortho (refer to Figure 7-1). For this reason the commercial processes to manufacture para-xylene are based on separation of the para isomer by freezing.

Because of the pioneering stage that para-xylene separation practices are in at the present, little has been published on the details of operation of the commercial plants. However, Figure 7-5 shows a continuous crystallization unit developed by Phillips at their Research Center. This process uses a scraped-surface crystallizer; however, evaporative crystallizers are also used. Additionally, to obtain a high-purity product, a system is often included which involves remelting of the product and counter-current washing of the crystallizers with this remelt.

The composition of the mixed xylenes and ethylbenzene stream is about:

Ethylbenzene	15 to 25	percent
Ortho-xylene	15 to 25	percent
Meta-xylene	35 to 45	percent
Para-xylene	12 to 22	percent

There are exceptions to this analysis; for example, the ethylbenzene content of Cosden's stream is 28 percent.[2] Only about two-thirds of the total para content is recoverable by crystallization, and since the original para portion of the total mixed stream is only 12 to 22 percent then generally about 0.1 pound of para-xylene is recoverable per pound of mixed xylenes and ethylbenzene.

In order to increase the recovery of para-xylene, a xylene-isomerization system is sometimes included in the processing scheme. In Figure 7-2, this is shown as Step No. 7. This isomerization step uses the effluent from the crystallizer as feed; this effluent contains about 7-9 percent para if the mixed xylenes are used as feed to the crystallizer and about 12-15 percent para if the ethylbenzene and ortho-xylene are removed from the feed to the crystallizer (thus leaving only meta and para). The isomerization unit brings the para concentration back to its equilibrium value of 19-20 percent if

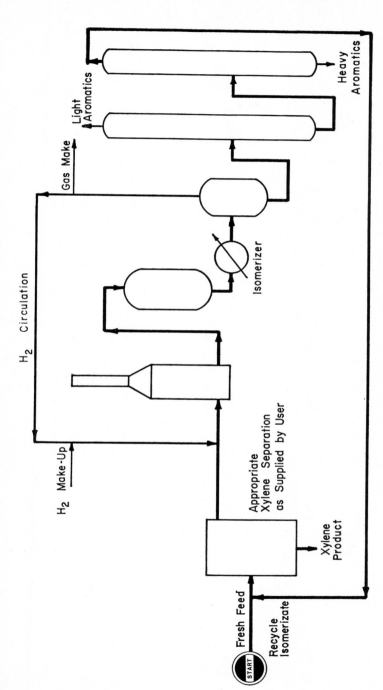

Figure 7-6. Xylene isomers can be made in this isomization process

a mixed xylene stream is being used and a somewhat higher figure if only the meta and para isomers are present. This isomerization process is shown in the form of a flow diagram in Figure 7-6. This process can also be used to produce other xylene isomers; in this case, a separation step appropriate to the desired isomer would replace the crystallization which is used to separate the para-xylene in Figure 7-2. However, as para is by far the most valuable isomer, this isomerization unit is ordinarily used to maximize para production. A flow diagram of the Suntide-Amoco para-xylene plant, which uses both crystallization and isomerization, is shown in Figure 7-7.

Much developmental work is being carried out in this field of para-xylene manufacture, and substantial improvements are expected in the next few years.

MARKETS

Mixed xylenes include the ortho, meta, and para xylene isomers plus ethylbenzene. Mixed xylenes are not used as a chemical but are used: (1) as a raw ma-

TABLE 7-2—Disposition of Recovered Mixed-Xylene Streams in U.S., 1965 and 1970

(in millions of gallons/year)

	1965	1970
Gasoline and solvents...................	258	209
Ortho-xylene...........................	41	55
Para-xylene...........................	55	166
Ethylbenzene..........................	41	60
Total..............................	395	490

NOTES: 1. Approximately 3.5 to 4.0 billion gallons a year of mixed xylenes are made in refineries, but only the quantities shown above are separated.
2. Ethylbenzene is included as a "mixed xylene" because it is usually found in a mixed-xylene steam.
3. The "gasoline and solvents" totals include any mixed xylenes oxidized by Amoco in the manufacture of iso-phthalic acid and terephthalic acid.

terial for one of the xylene isomers or ethylbenzene, (2) as a solvent, or (3) as a gasoline-blending stock. The recovery of ethylbenzene and ortho- and para-

xylene accounted for 34 percent of the mixed xylenes recovered in 1965 and will probably account for 57 percent by 1970; para-xylene will be the major gainer
(see Table 7-2 and Figure 7-8). Use as a solvent accounts for ¼ to ⅓ of the remainder, with gasoline
accounting for the other ⅔ to ¾ of the remainder.
These figures do not include the xylenes produced in
refinery reformers which are not recovered; this quantity
for the United States is about 9 to 10 times as large as
the quantity actually recovered as mixed xylene streams.

Essentially all of the meta-xylene that is produced goes
into the solvent and gasoline markets.

All of the ethylbenzene separated from the xylene
streams is used in the manufacture of styrene monomer,
either in the United States or abroad. This quantity was
about 41 million gallons in 1965, and if it keeps pace
with the general growth of styrene monomer, will be
60 million gallons in 1970. As more than 90 percent of
the ethylbenzene required in the United States is made
by the alkylation of benzene with ethylene, the market
requirements for ethylbenzene were discussed within
Part 3 of this series.

In line with the foregoing, a discussion of the chemical
uses of xylenes will be limited to the ortho and para
isomers.

Ortho-Xylene. Ortho-xylene is used almost solely in
the manufacture of phthalic anhydride and as a gasoline
blending stock. In 1965 some 330 million pounds of
U.S. ortho-xylene were consumed in the manufacture of
phthalic anhydride, both in the United States and
abroad; however, about 230 million pounds, or 70 percent of the total, were exported. The capacity to produce ortho-xylene in the United States is well over
600 million pounds/year; while this capacity did not
operate even close to the 100 percent mark, there was
a certain amount of ortho-xylene produced that was
dumped into the gasoline pools.

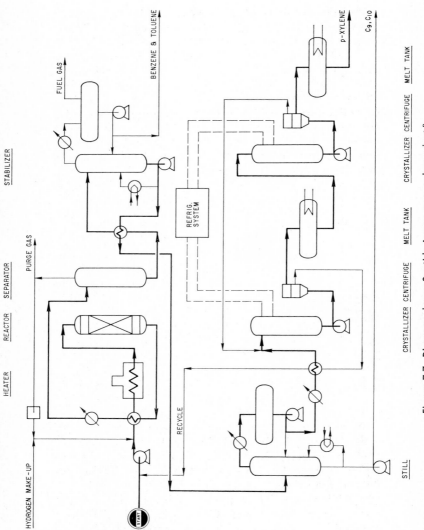

Figure 7-7. Diagram shows Suntide-Amoco para-xylene plant.[9]

Phthalic anhydride consumption in the United States is growing at the rate of 7 percent annually and will increase from 580 million pounds[11] in 1965 to a total of 820 million pounds in 1970. Most of this increase in phthalic manufacture will be based on ortho-xylene as a raw mtaerial, rather than naphthalene. Some existing phthalic anhydride plants using ortho-xylene consume more than one pound of ortho-xylene/pound of phthalic. However, the new phthalic plants being installed are expected to produce one pound of phthalic anhydride/pound of ortho-xylene.[3] Since the theoretical yield results in an ortho-xylene consumption of only 0.72 pounds per pound of phthalic, there will probably be some improvement in this 1:1 ratio in the future.

TABLE 7-3—U.S. Producers of Phthalic Anhydride Using Ortho-Xylene as a Feedstock

Company	Location	Phthalic Anhydride Capacity millions of pounds/year	Estimated Consumption of Ortho-Xylene—1965 millions of pounds/year
Allied[10]	El Segundo, Calif.	25	23
Chevron[10]	Perth Amboy, N.J.	30	29
	Richmond, Calif.	20*	0*
Monsanto[10]	St. Louis, Mo.	70**	..
Stepan[10]	Millsdale, Ill.	40	37
Tenneco[10]	Fords, N.J.	12	11
Totals		197	100

NOTES: * Reports indicate this unit was probably idle in 1965.
 ** Some reports indicate this unit can operate either on ortho-xylene or naphthalene.

A reasonable estimate is that 300 million pounds of ortho-xylene will be consumed in the United States in phthalic anhydride manufacture in 1970 but that exports will drop by 50 percent to a level of 110 million pounds. Hence, the U.S. production of ortho-xylene in 1970 will be about 410 million pounds, or a growth rate of 5 percent annually over the 1965 output of 330 million pounds.

Table 7-3 lists the U.S. phthalic anhydride producers using ortho-xylene as a feedstock; also an estimate of the 1965 consumption of ortho-xylene is shown.

Para-Xylene. Essentially all of the U.S. para-xylene produced as a chemical-grade material is consumed in the manufacture of either dimethyl terephthalate (DMT) or terephthalic acid (TPA). The predominant use of both of these materials is in the manufacture of polyester fibers. Until Chemstrand completed its polyesters-fiber plant late in 1965 all of the U.S. polyester manufacture was based on DMT as a raw material.

While there are other routes to DMT and TPA it appears that most of the U.S. capacity of these two materials will be based on para-xylene as a feedstock; thus the consumption of para-xylene in the United

TABLE 7-4—U.S. Producers of Dimethyl Terephthalate and Terephthalic Acid

Company	Location	Chemical Made	Capacity Millions of Pounds/Year	Estimated Consumption of Para-Xylene—1965 Millions of Pounds
Amoco[10]	Decatur, Ala.	DMT or TPA	200	0*
	Joliet, Ill.	DMT	100	?**
	Joliet, Ill.	TPA	40	23***
DuPont...............	Gibbstown, N.J.	DMT	120	90
	Old Hickory, Tenn.	DMT	200	120****
Hercules.............	Burlington, N.J.	DMT	60	45
	Spartanburg, S.C.	DMT	60	0*****
Mobil[10]..............	Beaumont, Tex.	TPA	75	5******
Tennessee Eastman....	Kingsport, Tenn.	DMT	70	50
Totals..............			925	340

    * Scheduled startup date—third quarter, 1966.
    ** Part or possibly all of this capacity is based on manufacture of a crude TPA by oxidation of a Para and/or mixed xylene stream; the crude TPA is then converted to DMT.
    *** Completed in 1965.
    **** Expansion completed in late-1965.
    ***** Scheduled for startup in early-1966.
    ****** Commercial plant completed end of 1965; pilot plant was operated in 1965.

States seems sure to follow the rapid growth projected for polyester fibers.

It is estimated that para-xylene consumption in the manufacture of DMT and TPA in the United States was 340 million pounds in 1965 and will be 1,200 million pounds in 1970. Net exports over imports of para-xylene were estimated to be 65 million pounds in 1965 and will probably be near zero in 1970; thus manufacture of para-xylene in the United States will be about 1,200 million pounds in 1970 versus 405 in 1965, or a growth rate of 24 percent annually.

Table 7-4 lists the U.S. producers of DMT and TPA and a rough estimate of their para-xylene consumption in 1965.

INDIVIDUAL COMPANIES

The capacity to produce mixed xylenes far exceeds the amount actually produced in 1965; therefore, it is difficult to estimate the actual production of the various companies. Nevertheless, it can be assumed that the companies with the largest capacities were also the largest producers; in this case the following companies were the major manufacturers of mixed xylenes in the United States in 1965. Each had a plant capacity in excess of 50 million gallons/year and it is believed that each produced more than 25 million gallons in 1965 (listed in approximate order of capacity):

Shell	Cities Service
Enjay	Chevron
Sinclair	Union Oil (formerly Pure)

Much of the mixed xylenes produced were used in gasoline pools and as a solvent. The gasoline-pool use was an internal one (well over 50 percent of mixed xylenes are used internally rather than sold) and the solvent sales were to many relatively small purchasers;

accordingly, there were no purchasers of mixed xylenes purchasing on the same scale on which the material is being produced.

The U.S. producers of ethylbenzene were listed in Part 3 of this series.

Turning to the xylene isomers, it is difficult to pinpoint 1965 production of ortho-xylene since the units were operating at about 50 percent of capacity. However, the following companies were believed to be the major manufacturers, with each producing more than 50 million pounds.

> Chevron
> Cities Service
> Hess
> Sinclair

On the purchasing side, some of the largest purchasers of U.S. ortho-xylene in 1965 were the export buyers. Stepan was the U.S. buyer purchasing the largest quantity of material—about 37 million pounds. Allied with purchases of about 23 million pounds was the only other major purchaser of ortho-xylene; the other major consumers—Chevron and Tenneco—were also manufacturers of ortho-xylene and supplied their own requirements.

Essentially all of the para-xylene that is produced is sold as there is very little internal use; the major sellers in 1965 were:

Chevron	115	million pounds
Sinclair	105	,, ,,
Enjay	95	,, ,,
Suntide (part Amoco)	35	,, ,,
Signal	15	,, ,,
Cosden	5	,, ,,
Total	370	,, ,,

DuPont is by far the dominant buyer of para-xylene in the United States, as indicated by this tabulation which shows estimated 1965 purchases:

DuPont	210	million pounds
Tennessee Eastman	50	" "
Hercules	45	" "
Mobil	5	" "
Total	310	" "

The difference between the 375 million pounds of para-xylene sold and the 310 million pounds bought is accounted for by export sales. (Amoco has half interest in a 50 million pound/year plant that was started up in 1965; it is operated by Suntide. Amoco also has internal use for para-xylene.)

These estimates of the amounts purchased and sold by the individual companies and the estimate of exports should be construed as being only very approximate.

HISTORICAL DATA

Tables 7-5, 7-6 and 7-7 present data for past years and estimates for future years for selected statistics for mixed xylenes, ortho-xylene, and para-xylene, respectively.

The data in these tables show a steady increase in the output of all three items, refer to Figure 7-9. Mixed xylene output was 395 million gallons in 1965 (about 2,850 million pounds). This compares with ortho-xylene output of 330 million pounds (Figure 7-10) and para-xylene output of 405 million pounds (Figure 7-11).

The U.S. production of ortho-xylene jumped dramatically in 1961 under the impact of large export orders; however, the 1965 output approximated the 1961 output. In the meantime, the price of ortho-xylene dropped from the 5 to 6¢/pound level down to the 2.6¢/pound level (Figure 7-12). This drastic drop in price resulted in a total value of ortho-xylene production of $8.8 mil-

TABLE 7-5—Historical Data: U.S. Production, Number of Producers and Sales Value of Mixed Xylenes

Year	No. of Producers From Petroleum	PRODUCTION millions of gallons/year			Sales Millions of Gallons/ Year	Average Sales Price ¢/Gallon	Total Value of Production Millions of Dollars
		Total	Tar Distillers and Coke-Oven Operators	Petroleum Operators			
1953**	9	113	10	103	66	26	29
1954**	12	110	10	100	66	27	30
1955**	12	108	12	96	78	27	29
1956	11	136	12	124	85	26	35
1957	15	127	12	115	83	27	34
1958	16	201	9	192	95	24	48
1959	16	241	8	233	129	22	53
1960	14	282	8	274	142	21	59
1961	19	257	8	249	124	22	57
1962	22	354	8	346	129	22	78
1963	24	335	7	328	131	19	64
1964	24	343	7***	336	154	18	62
1965*	24	395	7***	388	170	18	71
1970*	..	490	7	483	200	18	88

Source: U.S. Tariff Commission.
    * Estimates.
    ** The amount of mixed xylenes produced for use in blending motor fuels is excluded from the "Total Production" and "Total Production by Petroleum Operators" for 1953, 1954, and 1955; therefore, these totals for these years are not comparable with similar totals for the later years.
  *** Tar distillers' production estimated to be negligible.

TABLE 7-6—Historical Data: U.S. Production, Number of Producers and Sales Value of Ortho-Xylene

Year	No. of Producers	Production millions of pounds/year	Sales millions of pounds/year	Average Sales Price ¢/pound	Total Value of Production millions of dollars
1959***	3	62	**	**	**
1960	8	139	97	6.2	8.6
1961	12	318	251	4.8	13
1962	13	272	155	6.1	17
1963	13	304	221	3.3	10
1964	12	337	306	2.6	8.8
1965*	12	330	300	2.6	8.6
1970*	..	410	380	2.6	10–11

Source: U.S. Tariff Commission.
    * Estimates.
    ** Not reported.
  *** Production and sales data not available for years before 1959.

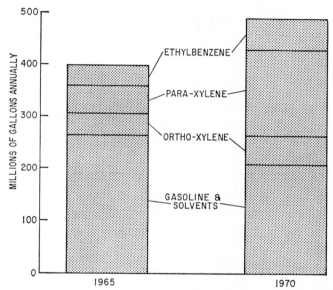

Figure 7-8. Here is how U.S.-mixed xylenes were used, 1965 and 1970

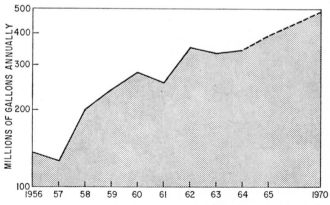

Figure 7-9. Mixed xylenes production in the U.S., 1956-1970

lion in 1965 compared with $17 million in 1962, refer
Figure 7-13. Because of large amounts of excess capacity
and a slow-growing market in the last few years, there
have been no new entries in the ortho-xylene manufacturing list since 1962. A final point is that well over
one-half of all ortho-xylene production is sold (as opposed to internal consumption).

The U.S. production of para-xylene has had a steady
but not spectacular increase in production in recent years,
with 1965 production of 405 million pounds representing

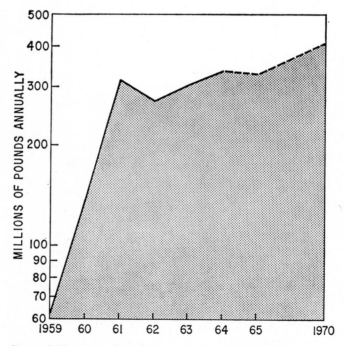

Figure 7-10. U.S. ortho-xylene production followed this pattern,
1959-1970

a 14 percent growth rate over the 1960 figure of 210 million pounds. The price of para-xylene dropped by one fourth from 1962 to 1963, with the resulting price being 9.1¢/pound in 1963 and about 8.0¢ in 1965. Refer Figure 7-14. The result was a total value of production in 1965 of about $32 million versus $32 million in 1961 and $29 million in 1960, refer Figure 7-15. Note that the

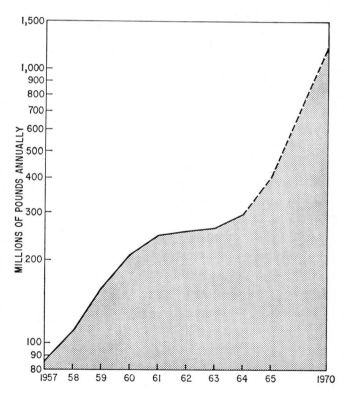

Figure 7-11. Para-xylene production in the U.S., 1957-1970

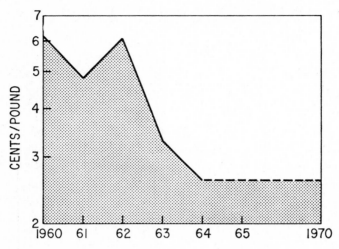

Figure 7-12. Sales price (average) for U.S. ortho-xylene, 1960-1970

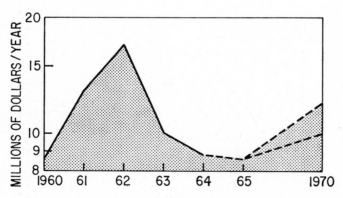

Figure 7-13. Value of ortho-xylene produced in the U.S., 1960-1970

TABLE 7-7—Historical Data: U.S. Production, Number of Producers and Sales Value of Para-Xylene

Year	No. of Producers	Production millions of pounds/year	Sales millions of pounds/year	Average Sales Price ₵/pound	Total Value of Production millions of dollars
1954**	5	59	42	17	10
1955***	5	..	..	..	..
1956***	2	..	..	..	..
1957	5	86	90	17	15
1958	5	106	80	16	17
1959	4	158	156	14	22
1960	4	210	218	14	29
1961	4	248	219	13	32
1962	5	256	272	12	31
1963	5	263	247	9.1	24
1964	5	296	313	8.6	25
1965*	6	405	375	8.0	32
1970*	..	1,200	1,000	5.0–7.5	60–90

Source: U.S. Tariff Commission.
    * Estimates.
  ** Production and sales data not available for years before 1954.
*** Production and sales data not available for these years.

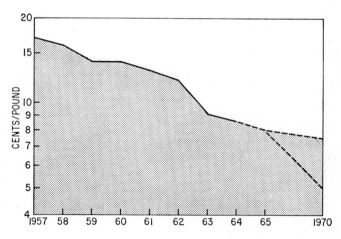

Figure 7-14. Average sales price of U.S. para-xylene, 1957-1970

number of producers of para-xylene has gradually increased; another item revealed in Table 7-7 is that virtually all of the para-xylene produced is sold rather than used internally.

ECONOMICS

Mixed xylenes are produced as a coproduct of toluene and usually benzene; thus its manufacturing cost cannot be ascertained accurately. In practice, however, more mixed xylenes are separated from refinery streams than are required for "deliberate" uses such as solvent markets or feed to a unit to separate ethylbenzene, ortho-xylene, or para-xylene. Therefore, the excess of xylenes made over the "deliberate" needs is added to the refiner's gasoline pool. Thus the mixed xylenes are valued at their gasoline value and any sales price must include the cost of pumping, storing, and loading as well as a profit. Xylenes are a premium blending stock, thus a price of slightly under 20¢/gallon is necessary before a refiner will sell mixed xylenes.

Ortho-xylene is separated from the other xylene isomers by distillation; recently, the excess capacity available for ortho-xylene separation has resulted in a sales price based on its gasoline blending value plus the handling charges. A producer of para-xylene may want the ortho-xylene removed before the meta and para isomers are fed to the crystallization unit, thus reducing the refrigeration load on this unit. However, if a para-xylene producer is short on xylene feedstock relative to his desired para-xylene production then he may want to include the ortho-xylene in the feed to the para unit. In this way the ortho isomer would be isomerized in the isomerization unit and thereby provide a greater production capability of para-xylene (this assumes the producer has an isomerization unit, which he would have if he were short of xylene feedstock to the para unit). Accordingly, the economics of ortho-xylene production are dependent on the over-all economics of the para-xylene production and markets.

Little has been published about the capital and manufacturing costs of para-xylene; however, a recent article presents the following information:[4]

Process costs (including utilities, labor, maintenance, and depreciation) in a large crystallization plant without isomerization unit, *excluding* rad material	= 2 to 3¢/pound
Processing costs for isomerization unit	= 2 to 3¢/pound
Total processing costs *including* raw materials for a combined crystallization and isomerization unit	= 5 to 10¢/pound

The major variables in determining manufacturing cost are plant size, the value of the mixed-xylene feed, and the credits that can be obtained from the byproduct streams. The importance of the byproduct streams is greatly reduced by the use of isomerization units, since without such a unit, the byproduct stream will be four to nine times as large as the para-xylene product.

To the processing costs must be added a return on investment. At present a para-xylene plant is reported to cost 6.8 to 10¢/pound of annual capacity.[5] It is believed that part of this variation is due to a different definition of what is included in the estimate. If a figure of 10¢/annual pound of capacity is used to include offsites, and if a return of 20 percent before taxes is satisfactory, then 2¢/pound for profit and about ½¢ for sales and administrative expenses must be added to the above processing cost to arrive at a required price. The result is 7½ to 12½¢/pound of para-xylene.

THE FUTURE

The output of mixed xylenes will continue to be in excess of that required for the "deliberate" end-uses, such as ortho-xylene, para-xylene, ethylbenzene, and solvents. Thus the sales value of mixed xylenes will continue to be related to its value as a gasoline blending stock; the future price of mixed xylenes is not expected to change radically from present day values, as the value of gasoline in the United States changes relatively slowly. With the present price of 18¢/gallon, and with a gradual growth to the 490 million gallon/year production level forecast for 1970, it appears that the value of mixed xylenes produced in the United States in 1970 will be slightly under $100 million.

The value of ortho-xylene will continue to be related to its gasoline-blending value as capacity to produce ortho-xylene will continue to exceed the chemical requirements for ortho-xylene even in 1970; thus little change is expected in the sales price of ortho-xylene. This is in spite of the fact that most of the new capacity to produce phthalic anhydride will be based on ortho-xylene as a feedstock. The total value of ortho-xylene produced in the United States will rise gradually to the $10-11 million level by 1970; however, this will still be below the peak of $17 million reached in 1962. Production, on the other hand, will be 50 percent greater in 1970 than in 1962!

Para-xylene output is projected to increase at the unusually high growth rate of 24 percent a year so the output in 1970 will be 1,200 million pounds compared with 405 million pounds in 1965, or 3 times as large. This large increase will be based on the growth of polyester fiber production. The meager information that has been published on para-xylene production and capital costs was discussed briefly in the section on "Economics"; these data seem to indicate a lower price level of 7½¢/pound and an upper price level of 12½¢/pound (the 12½¢/ pound figure is obviously unrealistic). However, para-xylene production economics are undergoing rapid change: Witness the fact that Amoco is completing a 200 million pound/year plant while there are a number of existing commercial plants less than 20 million pounds/year in capacity.

A recent study by the author showed that "On a long-term basis substantial increases in production rate will, in most cases, be accompanied by substantially lower prices."[6] The study further points out an example that

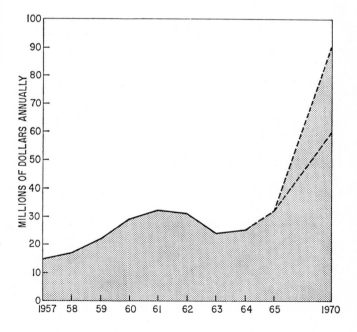

Figure 7-15. Value of U.S. produced para-xylene, 1957-1960

"if the chemical is expected to triple in volume over the next 6 to 10 years then its price may drop to two-thirds of today's market price."[6]

Based on the findings in this study it seems reasonable to expect a para-xylene price of 5.0¢/pound by 1970 compared with about 8.0¢ in 1965. Assuming the sales value is between 5.0 and 7.5¢/pound in 1970 then the total value of U.S. production will be $60 to $90 million, or substantially higher than the $32 million in 1965.

Thus para-xylene output will increase substantially and this will cause the total value of para-xylene produced to rise in spite of a major drop in price.

Literature Cited

1. Marwil, S. J., and S. J. Kolner, "Pulsed Column Purification of Para-Xylene," *Chemical Engineering Progress,* 59:60-65, February 1963.

2. Jenkins, Jerry G., "How Cosden Makes Polystyrene from Crude Oil," *The Oil and Gas Journal,* 63:78-86, January 18, 1965.

3. Guccione, Eugene, "New Fixed-Bed Process for Phthalic Thrives on o-xylene Feedstock," *Chemical Engineering,* 72:132-134, June 7, 1965.

4. Brown, David, "New Methods Cut Cost of Terephthalic Acid Manufacture," *The Oil and Gas Journal,* 63:103-107, February 8, 1965.

5. "Strong for Chemicals," *Chemical Week,* 96:24, February 6, 1965; and "Hercor Chemical Plans Para-Xylene Plant," *Chemical Week,* 97:29, July 17, 1965.

6. See Reference 1, Chapter 2.

7. See Reference 3, Chapter 1 for literature citations.

8. "Data Book on Hydrocarbons," Maxwell, J. B., D. Van Nostrand Co. Inc. New York City, 1950.

9. Brennan, Peter J., "Para-Xylene Now by Isomerization," *Chemical Engineering,* 73:118-120, January 17, 1966.

10. These companies have added or are adding additional capacity as of mid-1966.

8

Aromatics
and Derivatives

This chapter is a summary of the seven preceding chapters concerning the business and technical aspects of the "aromatics and derivatives" industry. "Aromatics and derivatives" for the purpose of this chapter consists of: benzene, cyclohexane, styrene, phenol, toluene, naphthalene, ortho-xylene and para-xylene.

Petrochemical processes accounted for 87 percent of the aromatics and derivatives produced in the United States in 1965 and are expected to account for 91 percent by 1970. The markets for this category of chemicals are growing at about 8 percent a year; fibers and plastics are the two outlets accounting for most of the growth.

Oil companies have become more important in this field, so that in 1965, 13 of the top 18 companies in the production of these chemicals were oil companies.

The three main variables involved in determining the economics of manufacturing aromatics and derivatives are the cost of the raw materials, the quality of the raw material, and the amount of capital required to build a plant. Labor is a relatively minor cost.

The massive price declines experienced in the markets for aromatics and derivatives over the past 10 years have to a large extent been halted; however, future price changes will still tend in the downward rather than the upward direction.[6] It is estimated that production in 1970 will be over 25 billion pounds, and with an average price in the 4.1 to 4.9¢/pound range, the value of production in 1970 will be between $1 and $1¼ billion. The three main areas of uncertainty facing this industry are: U.S. Government action on future requests for plants in Puerto Rico, proposed foreign-trade zones and foreign competition.

MANUFACTURE

Petrochemical processes accounted for 87 percent of the aromatics and derivatives produced in the United States in 1965. The remaining 13 percent consisted of

TABLE 8-1—Quantity of Aromatics and Derivatives Produced in 1965 in United States[1]
(from all sources)

Product	Production Millions Of Pounds/Year	Percentage Of Total
Benzene	6,050	35
Toluene	4,000	23
Styrene	2,875	16
Cyclohexane	1,820	10
Phenol	1,225	7
Naphthalene	813*	5
Para-xylene	405	2
Ortho-xylene	330	2
Totals	17,518	100

*Because of conversion of naphthalene from one grade to another, this figure may be overstated by as much as 10-20%.

benzene, toluene, and naphthalene from tar distillers and coke-oven operators; and phenol from all sources except the cumene and toluene processes.

TABLE 8-2—Value of Aromatics and Derivatives Produced in 1965 in United States[1] (from all sources)

Product	Value Millions Of Dollars	Percentage Of Total
Styrene	230	29
Benzene	215	27
Phenol	116	15
Toluene	94	12
Cyclohexane	73	9
Para-xylene	32	4
Naphthalene	27*	3
Ortho-xylene	9	1
Totals	796	100

*Because of conversion of naphthalene from one grade to another, this figure may be overstated by as much as 10-20%.

Of the total aromatics and derivatives produced from all sources, benzene and toluene are the two largest volume products (Table 8-1). On the other hand, styrene and benzene are the two products with the largest value of total production (Table 8-2 and Figure 8-1).

This section will be restricted to a discussion of the manufacture of aromatics and derivatives from an oil refinery. However, it should be recognized that the manufacture of these materials in a non-refinery setting would still utilize, with few exceptions, the same processes.

Figure 8-2 shows a very simplified flow diagram of a typical refinery without petrochemical manufacture. This refinery uses distillation to separate the crude oil into the various fractions; reforming to improve the quality of the gasoline; and cracking, alkylation, and polymerization to increase the quantity of gasoline and to improve its quality.

Figure 8-3 shows the same refinery with facilities added for the manufacture of all of the aromatics and derivatives discussed in this article. The chemistry is shown in Figure 8-4.

Most of the raw material for the production of aro-

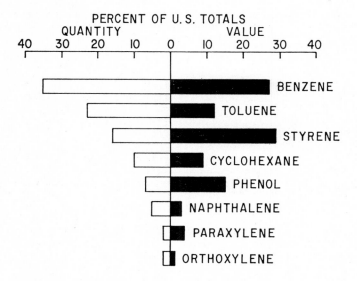

Figure 8-1. Relative quantity and value of aromatics and derivatives produced in United States in 1965.

matics and derivatives comes from the reforming unit; on the average for the whole industry, relatively minor quantities of raw material are obtained from ethylene plant byproducts and from catalytic cracking cycle oil.

The reformate from the reformer is fed to a solvent extraction unit in which aromatics are separated from the paraffins and residual naphthenes by dissolving in a solvent such as aqueous diethylene glycol or sulfolane. The non-aromatic raffinate is used in the gasoline pool, while the aromatics are stripped from the solvent. The aromatics are then separated by distillation in a series of columns into benzene, toluene, mixed xylenes, and alkyl-naphthalenes.

Benzene is either sold or used for the manufacture of cyclohexane, styrene, and/or phenol. A relatively simple

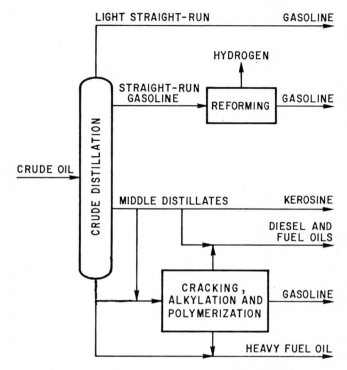

Figure 8-2. This simplified diagram shows a refinery without petro-chemical manufacture.

hydrogenation process is used for the manufacture of cyclohexane from benzene. A popular process uses a nickel catalyst and achieves almost total conversion of the benzene to cyclohexane.

The manufacture of styrene, on the other hand, is more complex. In this process, the benzene is alkylated with ethylene to form ethylbenzene. Either an aluminum chloride or a phosphoric acid catalyst can be used. A number of processing steps are required to separate the catalyst,

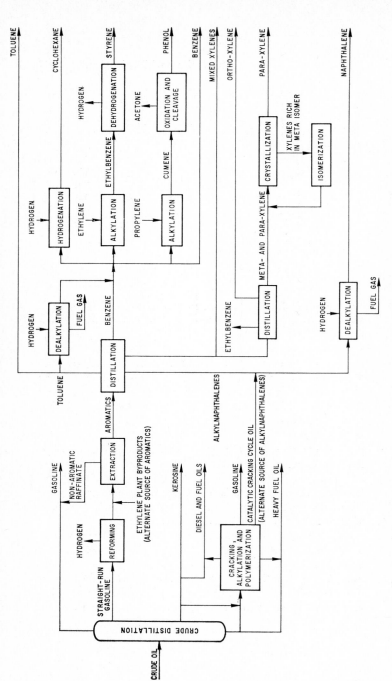

Figure 8-3. This simplified diagram shows a refinery with facilities for manufacturing aromatics and derivatives.

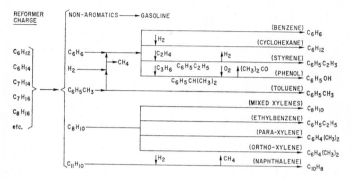

Figure 8-4. Shows the chemistry of manufacturing aromatics and derivatives.

ethylbenzene, and polyethylbenzenes. Ethylbenzene can also be recovered by distillation from the mixed xylene stream. The ethylbenzene is then fed to the dehydrogenation unit, where the ethylbenzene is dehydrogenated at 1200-1400° F in the presence of catalyst to form styrene. Since the conversion of ethylbenzene to styrene is in the 35 to 40 percent range, and since benzene and toluene are formed as byproducts, a distillation system consisting of a number of columns is required to separate the reactor effluent.

The third major petrochemical made from benzene is phenol. A number of processes are used for this purpose, but the cumene process and the toluene-based process are the only two considered to be petrochemical routes. The cumene route is by far the most popular and accounts for almost 50 percent of all synthetic phenol. In this process cumene is made by alkylating benzene with propylene; phenol and acetone are made in turn by oxidizing cumene and cleaving the hydroperoxide from the resulting molecule. The reactions are relatively simple, but extensive distillation systems are used to effect the separation of the reactor products.

The dominant use of toluene in chemical markets is in the manufacture of benzene by hydrodealkylation. In this dealkylation process, hydrogen reacts with toluene to form benzene and methane; the reaction and distillation systems are relatively simple.

The mixed xylenes can be dealkylated to produce benzene; however, this process is normally not economical in the United States. Instead the mixed xylenes are used as a raw material for the manufacture of the xylene isomers and ethylbenzene, or alternately sold as a solvent or used as a blending stock to improve the octane of gasoline. The separation of the xylene isomers and ethylbenzene is complicated by the fact that the boiling points are relatively close together. Nevertheless, ortho-xylene and ethylbenzene can be separated by distillation although tall columns are required. However, para-xylene boils only 1.4° F below meta-xylene and thus is separated by crystallization, as the melting point of para-xylene is about 100° F higher than that of meta-xylene. In order to increase the recovery of para-xylene, an isomerization unit is used to increase the para concentration in the meta byproduct stream so that it can again be fed to the crystallization unit.

The final petrochemical process to be discussed is the dealkylation of alkylnaphthalenes to produce naphthalene. Four different processes are available and all produce a refined grade of naphthalene; and all can operate on the higher-boiling materials from a reformer, or a catalytic cracker gas oil, or byproducts from steam cracking operations in which olefins are made. A feed purification system is usually needed with these latter two sources of raw materials in order to produce a feed sufficiently rich in aromatics. Less than 50 percent of the U.S. naphthalene is made from petrochemical sources, and it is anticipated that no more petro-naphthalene plants will be built in the foreseeable future.

Thus, a wide range of chemical processes including

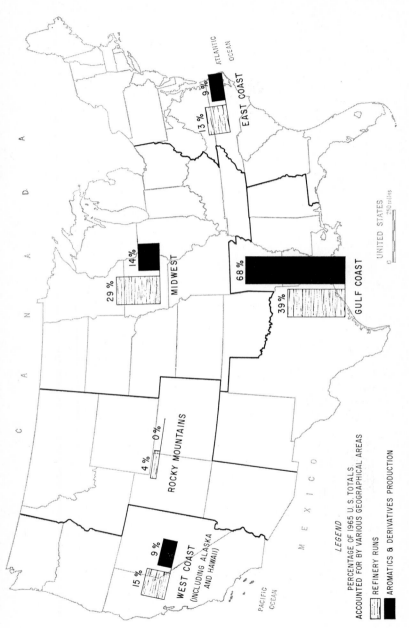

Figure 8-5. Compares refinery runs with production of aromatics, U.S., 1965, by geographical area.

LEGEND

PERCENTAGE OF 1965 U.S. TOTALS
ACCOUNTED FOR BY VARIOUS GEOGRAPHICAL AREAS

REFINERY RUNS

AROMATICS & DERIVATIVES PRODUCTION

TABLE 8-3—Typical Specifications or Inspections of Selected Products[3]

Benzene:

Purity (wt. percent)	99+
Freezing Point (°C)	5.44
Specific Gravity (60/60° F)	0.884
Pounds/Gallon (60° F)	7.4
Distillation (°C)	
IBP	79.5
DP	80.1
Flash (Tag Open Cup) °F	<40

Cyclohexane:

Cyclohexane Content, w%	99.8
Specific Gravity, (60/60° F)	.7835
(pounds/gallon—60° F = 6.52)	
Saybolt Color	+30
Sulfur Content ppm	1.0
Benzene, (w%)	<0.05
Phenols ppm	<1.0
Chlorides ppm	1.0
High Boiling Hydrocarbons, above and including toluene w%	<0.05
Other Non-Hydrocarbons vol. % excluding water	0.01
Distillation Range, (°C)	80.5—81.3

Toluene:

Purity (vol. percent)	99.7
Specific Gravity (60/60° F)	0.870
Pounds/Gallon (60°F)	7.25
Distillation (°C)	
IBP	110.4
DP	111.0

Orthoxylene:

Orthoxylene (vol. %)	96.5
Specific Gravity, (60/60° F)	0.883
Color, Saybolt	+30
Acidity	none
H2S and SO2	none
Olefins plus Saturates (vol. %)	0.3
Distillation, (°C)	
IBP	144.2
DP	145.4

Paraxylene:

Paraxylene (wt. %)	99.2
Specific Gravity, (60/60° F)	0.866
Paraffins (vol. %)	<0.1
Sulfur Compounds	nil
Acid wash color	0
Flash Point, TCC, °F	82
Bromine number	0.03
Distillation, (°C)	
IBP	138.0
DP	138.7

hydrogenation, dehydrogenation, alkylation, dealkylation, oxidation, and isomerization are used along with separation steps such as crystallization and distillation. These processing steps are not greatly different from the typical refinery units, except that the chemicals must be produced on the basis of chemical composition while refinery products are produced on the basis of boiling points and other physical characteristics.

Location of Plants. Figure 8-5 compares the refinery runs with the production of aromatics and derivatives for 1965 for each of the major geographical areas in the United States. The Gulf Coast area produced 68 percent of the U.S. aromatics and derivatives but accounted for only 39 percent of the U.S. refinery thruput. A combination of relatively naphthenic crude oil and relatively low gasoline values has made the Gulf Coast area a favorite location for aromatics plants. It is trailed by the Midwest, which has 14 percent of the aromatics and derivatives production and 29 percent of the refinery runs. The West Coast and the East Coast each account for 9 percent of aromatics and derivatives production. The West Coast leads the East Coast slightly in refining thruput, 15 percent of the U.S. total versus 13 percent.

Since many of relatively attractive refinery streams in the Gulf Coast area are now being processed for aromatics production, it is expected that over the next five years other areas in the United States will gain on the Gulf Coast in the production of aromatics and derivatives.

Product Specifications. Typical specifications or inspections data for benzene, cyclohexane, toluene, orthoxylene, and paraxylene are presented in Table 8-3.

MARKETS

The markets for U.S. aromatics and derivatives are projected to grow at slightly less than 8 percent a year until 1970, from an estimated 9.6 billion pounds in 1965 to 13.8 billion pounds in 1970. Refer to Table 8-4 and

TABLE 8-4—Markets for U.S. Aromatics and Derivatives, 1965 and 1970[1]

Market	MILLIONS OF POUNDS	
	1965	1970
Plastics	2,370	4,040
Exports	1,590	1,300
Fibers	1,580	3,390
Rubber	670	680
Coatings	450	590
Agricultural Chemicals	280	340
Detergents	250	220
Miscellaneous	2,380	3,200
Totals	9,570	13,760

These data exclude the amount of aromatics and derivatives used as gasoline blending stock and raw material for the manufacture of other aromatics and derivatives.

Figure 8-6. These estimates are the total amounts of aromatics and derivatives consumed, regardless of source, for all uses except gasoline and raw material for the manufacture of other aromatics and derivatives. However, material consumed in these "excluded" categories is included in the production totals in Table 8-5. These production totals also show a gain of slightly less than 8 percent a year, with a production of 17.5 billion pounds in 1965 and 25.3 billion pounds in 1970. This large difference between "markets" and "production" is primarily accounted for by benzene used in the manufacture of cyclohexane, styrene, and phenol; and toluene used in gasoline and in the manufacture of benzene.

Each of the major aromatics and derivatives discussed in this article, with the exception of ortho-xylene and para-xylene, has a diverse set of market outlets. This diversity is shown in a series of four charts: Figure 8-7 for benzene, cyclohexane, and styrene; Figure 8-8 for phenol; Figure 8-9 for toluene, and Figure 8-10 for the xylenes and naphthalene. These charts show only the more important outlets.

Each of the major outlets will be discussed briefly below. However, because of the complexity of the total market picture, the estimates which follow should be construed as being only approximations.

Plastics. This category includes polymers, plasticizers, and molding materials. It consumed about 2,370 million pounds of aromatics and derivatives in 1965, or 25 percent of the total; compared with an estimated 4,040 million pounds in 1970, or 29 percent of the total. This is a growth rate of about 11 percent. All materials will participate in this rapid growth, but styrene polymers will continue to be the largest single type of plastic in this category.

Exports. These accounted for 17 percent of the total in 1965, or 1,590 million pounds. They are expected to decline slightly by 1970, to 1,300 million pounds or only 9

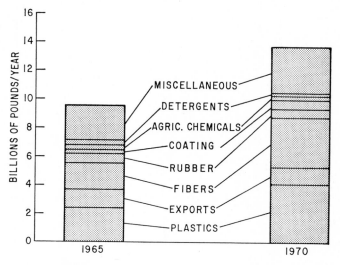

Figure 8-6. U.S. markets for aromatics and derivatives follow this pattern.

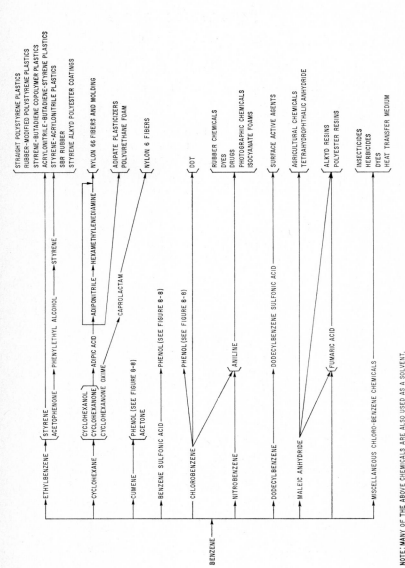

Figure 8-7. Major markets for benzene, cyclohexane and styrene.

NOTE: MANY OF THE ABOVE CHEMICALS ARE ALSO USED AS A SOLVENT.

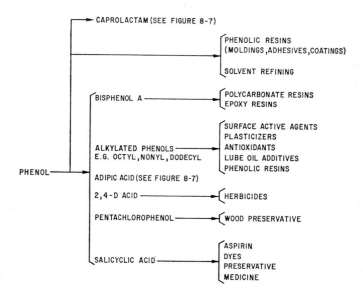

Figure 8-8. Phenol has these markets.

percent of the total of aromatics and derivatives. The accuracy of this estimate on exports rests to a large extent on the export performance of cyclohexane, which was the largest single export of the category in 1965 and will continue to be so in 1970.

Fibers. This category will displace "exports" as the number two category in the near future. This market is expected to grow at a rate of about 16 percent a year. Hence its 1970 consumption of aromatics and derivatives will be 3,390 million pounds, or 25 percent of the total, compared with an estimated 1965 consumption of 1,580 million pounds, or 17 percent of the total. Nylon fibers will continue to be the largest outlet, but polyesters will be the fastest growing outlet.

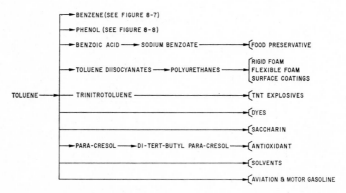

Figure 8-9. Toluene follows these major marketing patterns.

Rubber. Styrene used in SBR is the main outlet in this category and will continue to be so in the future; rubber chemicals account for the remainder. Total consumption of aromatics and derivatives in this category was about 670 million pounds in 1965 and will be approximately the same in 1970. Therefore, its share of the over-all market will drop from 7 percent in 1965 down to 5 percent in 1970.

Coatings. This category is projected to have a 6 percent growth rate thereby consuming 590 million pounds in 1970 versus 450 million pounds in 1965. Nevertheless, its share of the total aromatics and derivatives market will decline from 5 per cent in 1965 to 4 percent in 1970.

Other. Agricultural chemicals, detergents, and miscellaneous uses account for the remaining 2,910 million pounds in 1965; the bulk of this was in the miscellaneous category. Its 1970 consumption is estimated to be 3,760 million pounds, or 27 percent of the total compared with 30 percent of the total in 1965.

TABLE 8-5—Historical Data: U.S. Production and Sales of Aromatics and Derivatives[1]

| Year | Production Billions of Pounds/Year | | | Sales Billions of Pounds Year* | Average Sales Price ¢/Pound† | Total Value of Production Millions of Dollars |
	Total	Petro-chemical Processes	Pounds/ Others‡			
1953	5.4	2.9	2.5	3.7	6.7	363
1954	4.7	2.5	2.2	3.3	7.6	358
1955	5.9	3.1	2.8	4.1	7.9	468
1956	6.3	3.4	2.9	4.3	7.9	500
1957	7.0	4.2	2.8	4.5	6.8	474
1958	6.3	4.3	2.0	4.2	6.8	430
1959	7.4	5.2	2.2	5.6	6.9	508
1960	9.2	6.8	2.4	6.6	6.5	593
1961	10.2	8.0	2.2	6.8	6.3	640
1962	11.3	9.1	2.2	7.5	5.4	605
1963	13.0	11.0	2.0	7.9	4.7	610
1964	15.4	13.2	2.2	9.3	4.4	675
1965*	17.5	15.2	2.3	10.7	4.5§	796
1970*	25.3	22.9	2.4	15.2	4.1-4.9	1,050-1,250

* Estimates.

† Obtained by dividing "Total Value of Production" by "Total Production."

‡ Includes benzene, toluene, and naphthalene from tar distillers and coke-oven operators; and phenol from all processes except cumene and toluene processes.

§ This figure represents 1965 production value divided by 1965 production volume; the mix of chemicals produced in 1953 but valued at 1965 prices would result in an average sales price of 4.1¢/pound.

INDIVIDUAL COMPANIES

For many years the chemical companies were the leaders in the manufacture of derivatives of aromatics, primarily because of their leadership in styrene and phenol. In these early days the benzene was obtained from the coal tar industry. However, with the advent of refinery benzene in the 1950's, the petroleum industry gradually overtook the chemical industry in the manufacture of aromatics and derivatives. Listed below are all companies that produced approximately $20 million or more of this category of petrochemical in 1965. There are 18 companies on the list, and these 18 account for $590 million in annual production value, or 74 percent of the estimated total of $796 million. There are 5 chemical companies and 13 oil companies, and the output of these top 18 is

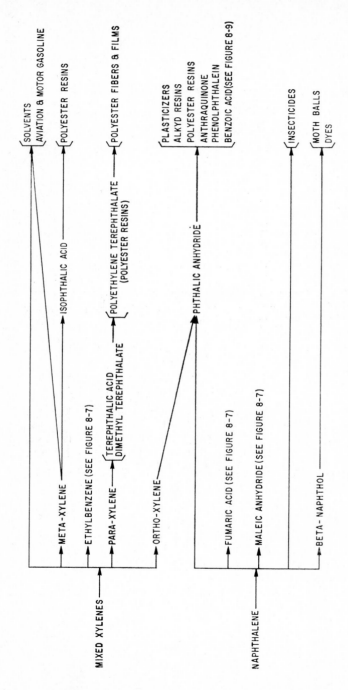

Figure 8-10. Major markets for xylenes and naphthalenes.

split approximately 40-60 between the chemical companies and the oil companies. However, Dow and Monsanto have retained their positions at the top of the list, primarily because of their large productions of styrene monomer. The importance of styrene monomer to the chemical industry is also indicated by the fact that two of the other three chemical companies on the list also produce styrene monomer—Union Carbide and Foster Grant.

Approximate value of 1965 production of aromatics and derivatives[1]	Company
$80 million	Dow and Monsanto
$60 million	Shell
$40 million	Enjay
$30 million	Amoco, Chevron, Gulf, Phillips, and Union Carbide
$20 million	Allied, Ashland, Conoco, Cosden, Foster Grant, Signal, Sinclair, Suntide and Union Oil

However, when we turn to the question of open-market sales, we find this area dominated by the oil companies. Only 2 of the top 10 companies are chemical companies, and these two account for about $40 million of sales versus about $200 million for the eight oil companies on the list.

Approximate 1965 sales of aromatics and derivatives[1]	Company
$40 million	Shell
$30 million	Enjay and Phillips
$20 million	Amoco, Ashland, Chevron, Dow, Gulf, Monsanto, and Suntide

The purchases of aromatics and derivatives are spread among many companies because of the many possible uses of benzene and phenol and the many producers of styrene polymer and phenolic resins. There are only four companies with purchases of about $20 million or greater, and all four of these are chemical companies.

Approximate 1965 purchases of aromatics and derivatives[1]	Company
$30 million	Dow, Du Pont, and Monsanto
$20 million	Union Carbide

HISTORICAL DATA

Table 8-5 presents data for past years and estimates for future years for selected statistics for U.S. aromatics and derivatives.

These data show a substantial increase in production of these chemicals in the United States; this increase is due solely to the production from petrochemical processes. The production from "other processes" has remained virtually constant since 1953. As a result petrochemical processes accounted for 87 percent of total production of 17.5

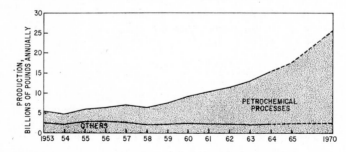

Figure 8-11. U.S. production of aromatics and derivatives, 1953-1970.

billion pounds in 1965 compared with only 53 percent of total production of 5.9 billion pounds in 1955. Refer to Figure 8-11.

Another important trend in the past 10 years has been the gradual reduction in the percentage of U.S. production sold rather than consumed by the manufacturer. This amount sold has dropped from the 70 percent level in 1955 to 61 percent in 1965. Refer to Figure 8-12. There has been a substantial amount of vertical integration in this business in the past 10 years so this has tended

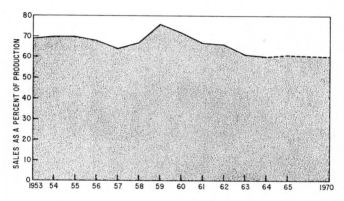

Figure 8-12. U.S. sales as a percentage of U.S. production, aromatics and derivatives, 1953-1970.

to reduce the amount of material sold on the open market. The fact that a substantial number of petroleum companies have entered the business as suppliers of aromatics to the chemical industry is the reason that the amount sold on the open market has remained as high as it has.

This rapid increase in growth of the total market for aromatics and derivatives has been accompanied by a substantial drop in average sales price in the United

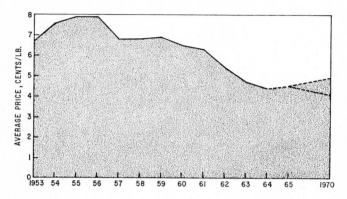

Figure 8-13. Average U.S. sales price of aromatics and derivatives, 1953-1970.

States, from 7.9¢ a pound in 1955 to 4.5¢ a pound in 1965. Refer to Figure 8-13. This drop in price has been caused by a drop in the price of the individual chemicals rather than by a change in mix of the individual chemicals. In fact the change in mix of chemicals has tended to keep the price higher, since the quantity of chemicals produced in 1953, but valued at 1965 prices, would have an average sales price of only 4.1¢ a pound.

The result of this combination of rapid growth in production volume and decline in average price has resulted in a gradual increase in total value of U.S. production, from $468 million in 1955 to $796 million in 1965. Refer to Figure 8-14. Thus, there has been a 200 percent increase in volume during the past 10 years compared with only a 70 percent increase in value of total production.

ECONOMICS

It is difficult to generalize on the economics of producing such a wide variety of chemicals as covered in the category of aromatics and derivatives. Thus, the reader should refer to the discussion of economics (in Parts 1-7) on the individual chemicals.

However, a simplified view of the basic economics is shown in Figure 8-15. The industry is built on the large availability of relatively cheap raw material. This cheap raw material is fed to the refinery reforming units and is worth about $1\frac{1}{2} \phi$/pound. Another way to view the raw material would be to consider it as being the gasoline blending stock from the reformer, in which case a slightly higher value would be assigned.

To this cheap raw material is added large amounts of capital and relatively small amounts of labor; the initial round of products vary in value from toluene at $2\frac{1}{4}\phi$/ pound to para-xylene at 8ϕ/pound. An example of the high capital-to-labor ratio encountered in this industry is the $41 million aromatics plant of Commonwealth Oil Refining Co. in Puerto Rico with only 350 workers; or a capital/labor ratio of $117,000 per man.[4]

The second round of processing steps again involves small inputs of labor; relatively large amounts of capital are involved with styrene and phenol manufacture as re-

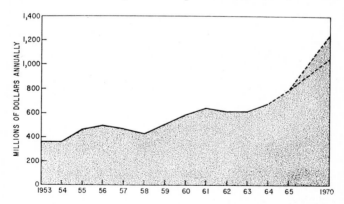

Figure 8-14. Total value of U.S. production of aromatics and derivatives, 1953-1970.

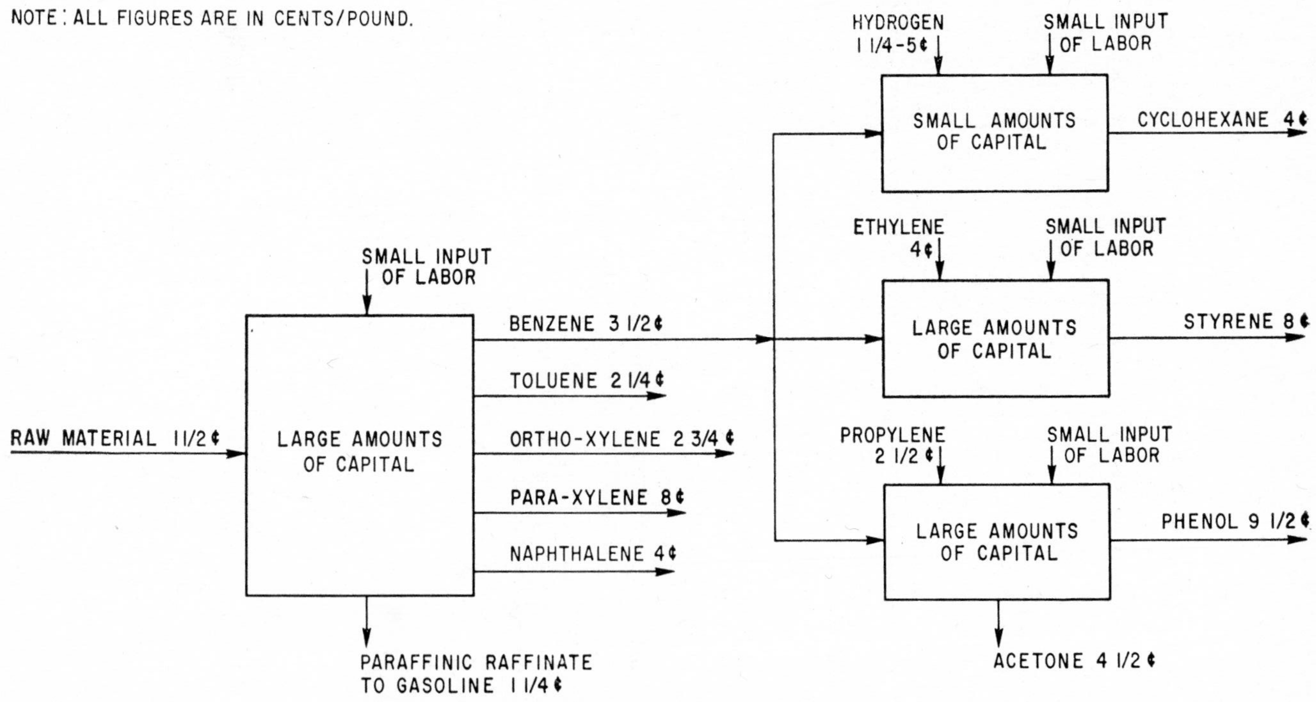

NOTE: ALL FIGURES ARE IN CENTS/POUND.

Figure 8-15. Economics of manufacturing aromatics and derivatives.

cent plants built in the United States have cost in the area of $10 million. Cyclohexane, on the other hand, requires relatively small amounts of capital as commercial plants can be built for approximately $1 million. The second round of processing also involves the inputs of additional raw materials; hydrogen at $1\frac{1}{4}$ to 5¢/pound in the case of cyclohexane, ethylene at 4¢/pound in the case of styrene, and propylene at $2\frac{1}{2}\text{¢}$/pound in the case of phenol. The result is products varying in value from cyclohexane at 4¢/pound to phenol at $9\frac{1}{2}\text{¢}$/pound.

Thus, there are three main variables involved in determining the economics of manufacturing aromatics and derivatives. The first is the cost of raw materials, especially the blending value of the aromatics to the gasoline pool of the individual refiners. The second main variable is the quality of the raw material, as a feedstock high in naphthenes will result in lower reforming and extraction costs per gallon of aromatics product.

The third main variable is the amount of capital needed to build a plant; this in turn is dependent on the size of the plant as great "economies of scale" can be obtained with larger plant sizes. That larger plants require considerably less capital per pound of product than do smaller plants is illustrated by the fact that a doubling of the plant size will result in a reduction of capital requirements of 25 percent/pound of product. The size of the plant in turn is limited by two factors: the availability of raw materials at a single location, especially for the reforming units to make aromatics; and the availability of markets for the products.

THE FUTURE

The markets for aromatics and derivatives will continue to expand at a faster rate than the Gross National Product of the United States. While the over-all growth rate of the markets for this category of chemicals will be about 8 percent/year between now and 1970, the bulk of the growth will be accounted for by plastics and fibers. These two outlets are expected to grow at rates of 11 percent and 16 percent, respectively, and thereby will account for 54 percent of the market in 1970 compared with 41 percent in 1965. Plastics consumption in the United States is presently less per capita than in West Germany and large potential markets exist in house construction and automobile manufacture.[5] The continued rapid growth of nylon fibers and polyester fibers accounts for the high growth rate of the fibers markets. Export markets will drop slightly on an absolute basis, but will account for only 9 percent of total markets by 1970 compared with 17 percent in 1965.

The increased production of aromatics and derivatives will come virtually exclusively from petrochemical processes, so that by 1970 some 91 percent of these chemicals will be petrochemicals as opposed to 87 percent in 1965. Although there will be increased vertical integration in the industry, the gradual decline in open-market sales as a percentage of the total production is expected to stop; thus these open-market sales should still be about 60 percent of production in 1970.

Plant sizes will continue to become larger and as a result production costs will gradually decline. Tending to offset this is the fact that the most economical sources of raw material for aromatics production have already been exploited in the United States, and hence future plants will be based on less attractive feedstock streams. There will continue to be substantial growth of the oil companies in this class of chemicals, so that the portion of the output accounted for by chemical companies will be relatively smaller in 1970 than in 1965. This combination of larger plants and more competition will tend to keep pressure on the price structures, especially for para-xylene, styrene, and phenol. However, for the category as a whole, the massive price declines experienced over the last 10 years have largely been halted so that average sales prices in 1970 will approximate those of 1965. Nevertheless, price changes will tend in the downward rather than in the upward direction.[6]

With 1970 production estimated to be in excess of 25 billion pounds, and with the average price between 4.1¢ and 4.9¢/pound, the value of total aromatics and derivatives produced in 1970 will be $1 to $1¼ billion. Refer to Figures 8-11, 8-13 and 8-14.

There are three main areas of uncertainty in the future of this industry; these are Puerto Rico, foreign-trade zones, and foreign competition. Each of these is discussed in more detail.

Puerto Rico. Commonwealth Oil has the world's largest aromatics plant in Puerto Rico and Phillips Petroleum is building a plant there now. These two plants together will produce about 150 million gallons/year of benzene, or the equivalent of about one-sixth of the U.S. market which will exist when the Phillips plant is completed. However, at the present time much of the output of Commonwealth Oil's plant is being sold in Europe, although this may not be the case several years hence.

The key ingredient which makes Puerto Rico potentially the lowest-cost manufacturing location in the world for aromatics is an import quota allowing a company to import the non-aromatic raffinate into the U.S. gasoline markets. For example, in Phillips' case, they received an import quota allowing them to import up to 24,800 barrels a day of gasoline into the United States for a period of 10 years. This import quota is worth about $11 million yearly.

With a raw material valued in the 4 to 5¢/gallon range in the Caribbean and with a third to a half of the plant output sold in the U.S. gasoline market at 1½ to 2 times the feedstock cost, the net raw material cost for aromatics production in Puerto Rico is very low. Thus, if the United States government were to give an import quota to any company wishing to build an aromatics plant in Puerto Rico, much of the world's future aromatics plants would be built there. However, the Phillips plant (of which the Puerto Rican government will own 25 percent will be the last plant for which an import quota is granted for at least a few years.

There are fundamental differences in the economics of Puerto Rico versus either a European plant or a plant in a foreign-trade zone in the United States. The key difference is that the plants in Puerto Rico have access to the relatively high-value U.S. gasoline market for the disposal of the non-aromatics byproducts. This high-value U.S. gasoline market is, of course, sheltered by the import quota system from gasoline obtained from the low-cost Venezuelan and Eastern Hemisphere crude oils. As do the aromatics plants in Europe, those located in U.S. foreign-trade zones would have access to low-cost feedstocks but would *not* have access to the high-value U.S. gasoline markets for the disposal of byproducts; thus these byproducts would have to be sold in the low-value foreign gasoline markets or alternately utilized in the manufacture of other chemicals. The present U.S. aromatics plants, of course, utilize high-value feedstock and use the high-value U.S. gasoline market for the byproducts.

These differences between Puerto Rico, Europe, U.S. foreign-trade zones, and U.S. present operations are highlighted in Figure 8-16.

Foreign-trade Zones. A number of chemical companies have followed Union Carbide's lead in asking for foreign-trade zones which would allow the importation of low-cost foreign naphtha as feedstock for ethylene and other basic chemicals. The naphtha would be exempt from U.S. oil import quotas, although the chemicals consumed in the United States would be subject to any U.S. tariffs.

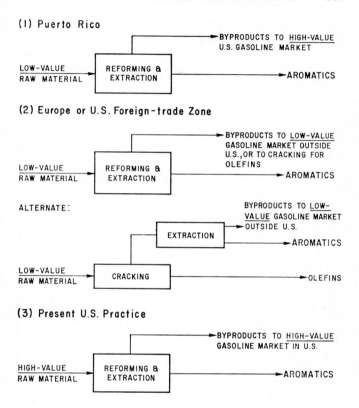

Figure 8-16. Cost advantage of manufacturing aromatics in Puerto Rico.

In addition to the differences discussed above between a foreign-trade zone and Puerto Rico, another major difference is that the foreign-trade zone proposals to date have resolved around the manufacture of olefins as the major products. However, it is likely that some of the companies would extract aromatic from the byproduct gasoline produced in naphtha cracking; or alternately would reform the naphtha, extract the aromatics, and then crack the paraffinic raffinate. In either case, manufacture of aromatics elsewhere in the United States by the extraction of higher-cost aromatics from marginally attractive refinery streams or the dealkylation of toluene would be postponed.

The U.S. government has granted nominal import quotas to petrochemical manufacturers for 1966. However, the value of these quotas is relatively small—it amounts only to about 5 percent of the manufacturing cost (including raw materials) of ethylene. Most industry observers expect major changes in this system in the future. The U.S. government still has the subject under intensive study, with particular reference to the effect on the U.S. balance of payments. The chemical companies are not satisfied with these small quotas and are insisting that they must have access to ample quantities of low-cost feedstocks from foreign sources in order to be competitive in the world economy; otherwise a greater percentage of their plants will be built abroad and thereby accentuate the U.S. balance of payments problem. The oil companies, especially the independent oil operators, are not happy with the situation because they believe it could lead to a more extensive breakdown in the oil import quota system.

U.S. crude oil production is in excess of 7 million barrels/day; approximately 600,000 barrels/day of naphtha would provide **100 percent** of the U.S. requirements of ethylene.

Foreign Competition. There has been a rapid buildup of aromatics plants in Europe in the last few years and this trend is continuing. Also, there will be large aromatics plants built in some of the major crude oil producing countries, such as Venezuela and Kuwait. The speed with which these foreign plants are built will determine the timing of the loss of the U.S. export markets. This is a major area of uncertainty in the market forecasts.

However there seems to be a trade and investment cycle in which plants are first built in the United States and products exported for a substantial period of time; but gradually plants are built abroad and U.S. exports drop in relative importance from their earlier peaks. Thus the U.S. exports of aromatics and derivatives will gradually decline as a percentage of total U.S. production.

Literature Cited

1. Calculated by author from data presented in previous seven articles in this series.

2. Production of aromatics and derivatives by geographical area was calculated by author from data in previous seven articles in this series. Refinery runs obtained from: *Oil and Gas Journal,* 64:160, January 31, 1966.

3. "Buyers' Guide Issue," *Chemical Week,* Part Two, 97:120, 170, 173, October 16, 1965.

4. Richard Martin, "CORCO Now Operating World's Largest Aromatics Plant," *Petro/Chem Engineer,* 38:40-48, February 1966.

5. "Meeting the Demand for Plastics," *Petroleum Press Service,* 33:62-64, February 1966.

6. This statement is based on assumption of reasonably-stable price level in United States economy in the future.

Index